Glossary of the Environment

Conseil International de la Langue Française

adapted by Paul Brace

foreword by René Dubos

The Praeger Special Studies program, through a selective worldwide distribution network, makes available to the academic, government, and business communities significant and timely research in U.S. and international economic, social, and political issues.

Glossary of the Environment

With French and German Equivalents

PRAEGER SPECIAL STUDIES IN INTERNATIONAL ECONOMICS AND DEVELOPMENT

Praeger Publishers   New York   London

Library of Congress Cataloging in Publication Data

Conseil international de la langue française.
    Glossary of the environment.

    (Praeger special studies in international economics
and development)
    Includes index.
    1. Human ecology—Dictionaries.   2.   Environmental
protection—Dictionaries.   I. Brace, Paul.   II.   Title.
GF4.C66   1977   301.31'03   76-19547
ISBN 0-275-23760-5

PRAEGER SPECIAL STUDIES
200 Park Avenue, New York, N.Y., 10017, U.S.A.

Published in the United States of America in 1977
by Praeger Publishers,
A Division of Holt, Rinehart and Winston, CBS, Inc.

789   038   987654321

© 1977 by Conseil International de
la Langue Française

Printed in the United States of America

FOREWORD
René Dubos

The word environment became part of everyday language less
than two decades ago, and its meaning is far from clear. In fact, it
has evolved and continues to evolve, in part due to an increase in
scientific knowledge but even more as a result of changes in the mood
of the general public. During the 1960s, for example, the word environment evoked chiefly pollution, the depletion of natural resources,
overpopulation and crowding, the thousand devils of the ecological
crisis. In contrast, there is greater emphasis today on the positive
qualities of the environment—on those physical and social characteristics that contribute to the quality of life.

The scientific language of the environment presents more funda-
mental difficulties. At first glance, there seems to be no problem in
differentiating between organism and environment. The word environment is used to denote the setting in which the organism develops and
functions, and refers to all the factors of the external world that affect
biological and social activities. From a narrow scientific point of
view, therefore, the human skin or the cellular wall sharply separates
the living organism—human or microbial—from the external world.

The distinction between organism and environment becomes
blurred, however, when one considers living things and external world,
not as separate static entities, but as interacting dynamic components
of complex dynamic systems. This is particularly true of the human
environment, viewed by the biologist, the physician, the farmer, the
forester, the engineer, the urbanist, the sociologist, the painter, the
poet, each from his own specialized point of view, and referring to
it with his own specialized language.

All human beings, furthermore, are conditioned in their
response to the physical and social universe by education and parental
training, as well as by the traditions, myths, and rituals of their
society. The individual attitudes they thus develop constitute the basic
premises according to which they organize their perceptions of the
outer world and create for themselves a conceptual environment.

In view of these complexities and individual differences, it is
not surprising that the language used by environmentalists often lacks
precision. The meaning of their words differs according to past expe-
rience and professional specialization, and evolves with changing
social conditions.

The glossary presented here would have been much simpler
and easier to prepare if it had dealt only with the environment "out

there, " unrelated to human life. But it would then have failed to reflect the most interesting and most important problems of the environment, namely, those posed by the rich interplay between living things and external forces, an interplay that has both destructive and constructive manifestations. Mr. Brace and his colleagues have wisely decided to structure their glossary around this interplay and have thereby greatly contributed to the precision and quality of writing about the living environment.

A few years ago, a research team was assembled by the U.S.
Corps of Engineers to work on its Northeast Water Supply Study. On
the team were environmental engineers, soil physicists, soil chem-
ists, agricultural engineers, and agronomists. According to Water
Research in Action, "As could be expected, communications were
hampered by jargon; everyday language for one discipline was foreign
to that of another."*

The World Health Organization reported in January 1976:

> Participants at a recent WHO seminar at Katowice in
> Poland noted a "communications gap" between environ-
> mental pollution specialists and health planners. They
> concluded that planners and environmental experts often
> did not know how to communicate their information to
> one another or to the politicians.
>
> One effect of this was that theoretical knowledge of
> the problems involved was outstripping the practical
> capacity to get results.†

The recent evolution of environment as a distinct discipline has
given new meanings or nuances to established terms, and created new
ones. Understanding environmental terms is the first and prerequisite
step in understanding the structure of natural and human ecological
systems, their interrelations and processes.

People of many backgrounds and interests are involved in
influencing and making decisions affecting the environment: politicians,
lawyers, judges, land developers, builders, highway engineers,
journalists, planners, conservationists. They must now deal daily
with a vocabulary heretofore in the exclusive domain of researchers
and academicians. The concerted action required to manage the environment involves different disciplines using terminologies which,
although specialized, are sometimes ambiguous, imprecise, or
obsolete in the environmental context. The environmental generalist
needs to understand the specialists, and the specialist needs to

*Donald Dean Adrian, Water Research in Action I (May 1976):
2-3.

†"Pollution and Planning," World Health (January 1976): 32.

understand specialists in other fields when dealing with the broad context of the environment.

This glossary was developed to respond to these needs for better understanding and communication. Key words were selected from a large number of terms from many disciplines—from acoustics to genetics and sociology to radiology—contributing to the body of environmental knowledge, and defined in their environmental context. Their selection and definition must be viewed with the awareness that terminology, particularly when applied to the environment, is by nature both relative and evolutionary.

Terms were selected for their major, direct relevance to the environment.

Words in common use in the language, without a distinct environmental interpretation (for example, highway, thermometer) were generally excluded, as well as highly specialized terms, despite their environmental connotation.

Definitions reflect the distinct, sometimes newly established, environmental interpretations and implications of the terms, and exclude nonenvironmental meanings.

A qualifier generally precedes a term to indicate its specific field, although often not used by the specialists in that field (for example, radiation exposure, sound-intensity level).

Definitions often include closely related terms (underscored) which are defined within this context.

An entry that refers the reader to another term appears underscored and defined within the referenced term's definition.

An asterisk after a word or phrase in a definition indicates that there is a main entry for the word or phrase, where it is defined.

Synonyms are identified following the definitions, and are listed alphabetically under separate reference entries.

The noun form of a term is generally listed in preference to the adjective or verb forms (for example, dominance, symbiosis).

More than one environmental definition is given for some terms, with the corresponding disciplines indicated.

CONTENTS

	Page
FOREWORD René Dubos	v
PREFACE	vii
EDITORIAL NOTES	ix
GLOSSARY OF THE ENVIRONMENT	1
FRENCH AND GERMAN EQUIVALENTS	83
INDEX	105
ABOUT THE AUTHORS	119

Glossary of the Environment

ABIOTIC
See Biotic

ABSORBED DOSE
Amount of energy from ionizing radiation* absorbed by a substance,
medium, or organism, at a given point and for a given period. Specific absorbed dose: Amount of energy per unit mass of irradiated
material. Unit of measurement: rad (energy absorption of 100 ergs
per gram). Radiological dose: Total amount of energy absorbed by
an individual.

ACCLIMATATION
Adjustment of an organism or population to a new climate* and/or
other environmental condition. This adjustment requires adaptation*
when the new condition is beyond the organism's tolerance limit.*
Naturalization: Forced acclimatation, usually induced by man.
Syn.: Acclimatization.

ACCLIMATIZATION
See Acclimatation

ACCUMULATION
Progressive increase in the content of a substance or agent in an
organism or medium, through successive or continuous ingestion,
secretion, deposit, or exposure,* and its retention due to insufficient
corresponding elimination. Concentration: Result of this process;
accumulated content in proportion to the total mass of the receiving
organism or medium. Cumulative effect: Physiological result of the
concentration of a pollutant* in an organism or medium, and of the
persistence* of its effects. Trophic accumulation: Passage of a
pollutant through trophic levels* of a food chain* with cumulative
retention by organisms. Peak concentration: Maximum instantaneous
quantity of substance or agent in a medium, measured over a specified
period at a determined point.

---

* Defined as a main entry in alphabetical order.

ACID SMOG
See Smog

ACOUSTIC DISTURBANCE
Single intruding noise* distinguishable from other ambient noises.*

ACOUSTIC POWER
See Sound power

ACOUSTICS
Field of science, derived from physics, that deals with sounds,* their
nature, production, transmission, reception, and effects.

ACOUSTIC SIGNAL
Acoustic disturbance* used to convey information.

ACOUSTIC VIBRATION
Motion of particles in a medium.

ACTIVATED CARBON
Highly porous carbon, usually obtained by carbonization of vegetal
matter or peat and chemical activation, used for filtration and other
fluid purification processes. Syn.: Activated charcoal.

ACTIVATED CHARCOAL
See Activated carbon

ACTIVATED SLUDGE
See Sewage sludge

ADAPTATION
Process and result of morphological, physiological, and psychological
changes undergone by an organism or a population,* in order to carry
out its life functions most effectively and with least discomfort,*
under given environmental conditions markedly different from those
prevailing during the previous stage of life, or previous generation.
Degree of adaptability: Relative ability of an organism or population
to adapt to new and unfavorable environmental conditions. Also: estimated evolutionary potential of a species, genus, or family.

ADJUVANT
Substance added to a product to increase its effectiveness, improve
its characteristics, or facilitate its manufacture.

ADJUVANT TREATMENT
Complementary treatment that enhances the effectiveness of a basic treatment.

ADULTERANT
See Impurity

AERATION
Exposure* of a substance or medium to the action of air or other gases, or introduction of air into it, by various natural or artificial processes, often used for purification purposes. Aerator: Device used for aeration.

AERATOR
See Aeration

AEROBIC
Requiring air or free oxygen to live or develop, such as certain bacteria. Antonym: Anaerobic.

AEROSOL
Suspension* of solid or liquid particles of micrometric dimensions in a gaseous medium.

AEROSOL PROPELLANT
Gas, such as a fluorocarbon, or vapor under pressure in a valved container (spray can), used as a carrier to spray a substance such as a cosmetic or household cleaner. Certain of these propellants are believed to contribute to the destruction of the ozone layer of the atmosphere* (which absorbs ultraviolet radiation of the sun), and thus increase the risks of skin cancer.

AGE
Chronological age: Time elapsed since the birth of an individual, expressed in years and smaller units of time. Biological age: Measure of the fatigue* and deterioration of tissues and organs of an individual through the aging process, expressed by reference to an arbitrary norm of chronological age for that condition. Mental age: Degree of mental development of an individual evaluated by reference to an arbitrary norm of chronological age for that stage of development.

AGE INTERVAL
See Population composition

AGE-SPECIFIC BIRTH RATE
See Birth rate

AGE-SPECIFIC DEATH RATE
See Mortality rate

AGING PROCESS
See Age

AGGREGATE
Mineral material composed of particles of various sizes held together
by finer organic or mineral material.

ALGA
Thallophyte containing chlorophyl; a primitive, generally aquatic plant
group including diatoms and sea weeds. Important for its function of
supplying oxygen from the atmosphere by photosynthesis. Almost
exclusively used in its plural form, algae. Algae bloom: Polluting
concentration of microscopic algae caused by heavy nutrient* content
in water.

ALGAE BLOOM
See Alga

ALGICIDE
See Pesticide

ALLERGEN
Antigen, such as pollen, drug, or food,* inducing an allergy* in an
organism upon contact.

ALLERGY
Pathological reaction of certain hypersensitive organisms induced by
contact with a given allergen.* This reaction may be intensified
(anaphylaxis) or attenuated (immunity) by repeated contact.

ALLOGENIC
Caused by factors external to an ecosystem.*

ALLUVIAL DEPOSIT
See Alluvium

ALLUVION
See Alluvium

ALLUVIUM
Soil* particles, rocks, and debris resulting from erosion,* transported
and deposited by a stream on the valley floor. Syn.: Alluvial deposit,
alluvion.

AMBIANCE
Environment* viewed from its relation to a point of reference in time and space, such as a person or a phenomenon.

AMBIENT NOISE
Composite of all sounds* from close and distant sources, pervasively present over a representative period in a given auditory environment.*

AMMONIFICATION
See Nitrogen cycle

ANAEROBIC
See Aerobic

ANAPHYLAXIS
See Allergy

ANIMAL ASSOCIATION
See Biocenose

ANIMAL COMMUNITY
See Biocenose

ANOMALY
Congenital* malformation reducing the performance of vital functions and/or exhibiting variance from the normal structure of the organism.

ANOMIE
Abnormal social behavior* of an individual or a group, with characteristics such as disorientation, alienation, rejection of accepted values, and lack of conformity to the normative standards* of the society,* often regarded as resulting from life in an urban environment.*

ANTITOXIN
See Toxin

APARTMENT HOUSE
See House

AQUACULTURE
See Aquiculture

AQUICULTURE
Commercial production of aquatic plants and animals by cultivation and other development of the marine and fresh water environment.

Syn.: Aquaculture. Not to be confused with hydroponics: Cultivation
of plants without soil,* in a nutrient* solution with or without inert
matter support such as sand.

AQUIFER
Porous soil stratum capable of storing and yielding through springs*
or wells important amounts of water, sometimes contained between
impermeable layers, and located in the zone of saturation* (where
interstices are filled with water), below the zone of aeration* (where
interstices are largely filled with air and the water is not under hydro-
static pressure). Aquifers can be depleted, recharged, or polluted.

ARTIFICIAL RADIOACTIVITY
Radioactivity* created in a substance by bombarding it with ionizing
radiation* from nuclear reaction.*

ASSIMILATION
Transformation of nutrient* into protoplasm by the cells of a living
organism.

ATMOSPHERE
Gaseous layer surrounding the earth and other planets

ATMOSPHERIC SCIENCES
See Meteorology

ATOMIC PILE
See Nuclear reactor

ATOMIC REACTOR
See Nuclear reactor

AUDIO FREQUENCY
Frequency of a vibration normally audible to man (acoustic vibration*).
Audio frequencies range approximately from 15 to 20,000 cycles per
second (cps) or hertzes (Hz). Frequencies below and above the audio
range are called infrasonic and ultrasonic respectively.

AUDIOGRAM
Graphic representation of hearing thresholds as a function of
frequency.

AUDIOMETER
Instrument for the measurement of hearing characteristics, in particular the hearing level.*

AUDIO RANGE
See Audio frequency

AUDITORY ENVIRONMENT
Totality of sounds* perceived over a continuing period within a specific
space, also referred to as environmental noise.

AUDITORY SENSATION AREA
Area of an audiogram* contained between the curves describing the
threshold of audibility* and the threshold of pain.*

AUTECOLOGY
See Ecology

AUTOCHTHONOUS
See Indigenous

AUTOTROPH
Organism that derives organic nutrients* from inorganic substances
by chemosynthesis* or photosynthesis.*

BACKGROUND NOISE
Ambient noise* exclusive of any specific acoustic disturbance* or source
noise under observation.

BACKGROUND RADIATION
Sum of ionizing radiation* received at a given point including natural
radiation,* cosmic radiation,* and radiation from other sources.

BACTERIAL TOXIN
See Toxin

BACTERICIDE
See Pesticide

BENTHIC
See Benthos

BENTHOS
The environment formed by the ocean floor, especially in its deepest
parts, the bottom layer of water, and its flora and fauna. Adj.:
Benthic.

BIOCENOSE
Distinctive group of animal and vegetal species living under the same
general environmental conditions and having their habitats* in the

same space, or biotope,* in a relatively stable relationship and
evolution. Further divided into plant community and animal community,
often distinguished by the dominant* plant association or animal association. Syn.: Biotic* or ecological community.

BIOCHEMICAL OXYGEN DEMAND
Amount of dissolved oxygen required by anaerobic microorganisms
necessary to decompose the organic solids present in liquid waste.*
Abbreviated: BOD. Measurement used to estimate the oxygen depletion
of the water due to the deterioration of organic matter. The standard
laboratory BOD test* of liquid waste before or after treatment determines the consumption of oxygen in milligrams per liter of liquid over
a five day period (BOD_5) at 20°C.

BIOCIDE
See Pesticide

BIODEGRADABLE
Susceptible to breaking down into simpler molecules by microorganisms.* Biodegradability of waste* is essential to its effective processing and disposal.

BIODYNAMIC
See Ecological interaction

BIOGEOCHEMICAL CYCLE
Process of biological, geophysical and/or chemical transformation of
matter into successive states, in an uninterrupted and circularly
repeated series of interactions which provide the dynamic linkage of
the parts of the earth (lithosphere,* atmosphere,* hydrosphere,*
biosphere*), and cause the regeneration of natural resources, critical
to the maintenance of life. Biogeochemical cycles, such as nitrogen,*
carbon,* or water cycles, are varied and complex, taking place over
a broad range of space and time scales, and are subject to disruption
by pollution.*

BIOGEOGRAPHY
Field of science that deals with the distribution of animal (zoogeography) and plant (phytogeography) species on the earth, its causes and
changes.

BIOLOGICAL AGE
See Age

BIOLOGICAL BALANCE
Stable and constant state in the structure and operation of an
ecosystem* achieved through a dynamic equilibrium of ecological
interactions* among the animal and vegetal species coexisting in a
biotope.* Maintenance of biological balance depends heavily upon the
diversification of the biocenose.*

BIOLOGICAL CONTROL
See Pest control

BIOLOGICAL CYCLE
Evolution and development of an organism, individual, group, or
population through a series of successive stages over its lifetime, or
returning to a previous or primary stage, as in a seasonal cycle.

BIOLOGICAL HALF-LIFE
Period of time during which the quantity or concentration* of a particular substance present in a body or biological system is reduced by
half through biological processes of elimination.

BIOLOGICAL INDICATOR
Individual organism, animal or vegetal species such as fish, lichen,
or algae,* or community of organisms, whose presence and morphological and pathological conditions enable an observer to derive certain
specific information regarding environmental factors and pollutants.*

BIOLOGICAL PRODUCTION
Organic matter or energy equivalent resulting from the growth and
reproduction of a given organism, species, or population, in an
ecosystem* at one trophic level,* measured by its biomass* or energy.
Primary production is by autotrophs,* mostly plants and bacteria;
secondary production, by heterotrophs,* mostly animals. Biological
productivity: Rate of biological production during a given period of
time for a unit of area, commonly measured in calories per square
meter per year.

BIOLOGICAL PRODUCTIVITY
See Biological production

BIOLOGY
Field of science that deals with living organisms and life processes.

BIOMASS
Amount of animal or vegetal matter or tissue contained in the popu-
lation of a species in a given unit of area or volume of habitat.*
Measurement used for food chain* analysis.

9

BIOMASS PYRAMID
See Ecological pyramid

BIOME
Large geographic area, partly determined by latitude and altitude,
constituting a complex natural community such as deciduous forest or
desert, characterized by distinctive ecological associations and biological forms, and dominant* animal and vegetal species. Subjected
to ecological succession terminating in a climax, or mature and stable
community at its final stage of natural evolution.

BIOSPHERE
Parts of the earth where life can be maintained, and supported by
ecosystems* (biotic* environment*), including the lower part of the
atmosphere,* the upper part of the lithosphere,* and the hydrosphere.*
By extension, the totality of living matter on earth.

BIOTA
Flora and fauna of a particular region.

BIOTIC
Characteristic of, or relating to, living organisms. Antonym: Abiotic:
Free from living organisms; not capable of supporting life; inorganic
matter.

BIOTIC COMMUNITY
See Biocenose

BIOTOPE
Area of varying size with generally uniform and constant environmental conditions such as a swamp or a cave, suitable for a particular
biota* or biocenose.*

BIRTH RATE
Ratio of babies born to a population during a given period in a specified
area. Generally expressed as crude birth rate (number of births per
thousand population per year). More meaningful indexes of natural
population growth are age-specific birth rate (number of births per
thousand women of a given age group), from which can be obtained
the fertility (total number of births to all women of child-bearing age);
and net reproduction rate (number of female births of all women of
child-bearing age, making allowance for female death rate). Birth
rate differentials between populations* are related to their composition*
and are due to social (population policies) and individual (family
planning*) actions, rather than physiological reproduction capacity
(fecundity).

BLACK TIDE
See Oil pollution

BOD TEST
See Biochemical oxygen demand

BUFFER STRIP
See Open space

BUFFER ZONE
See Open space

BY-PRODUCT
See Waste

CAPITAL GOOD
See Good

CARBON CYCLE
Biogeochemical cycle* of carbon element, consisting primarily of
conversion of carbon dioxide of the atmosphere* by plants through
photosynthesis* to organic compounds, then metabolized by animals,
and returned to the atmosphere as a product of respiration, waste,*
or bacterial and chemical decomposition.

CARCINOGEN
Substance or agent inducing cancer in an organism upon contact.

CARRYING CAPACITY
Maximum size of stable populations* of given species that can be
supported by the ecosystem* of a particular area, without depletion
of the natural resources* and deterioration of the quality of the
environment* or the well-being* of individuals.

CASE FATALITY RATE
See Mortality rate

CATCHMENT AREA
See Drainage basin

CHEMICAL OXYGEN DEMAND
Amount of dissolved oxygen required for chemical digestion of organic
matter present in liquid waste.* Abbreviated: COD. COD tests permit
estimation of the amount of oxidizable material in liquid waste* before
or after treatment.

CHEMICAL WEATHERING
See Decomposition

CHEMOSYNTHESIS
Synthesis of organic substances by microorganisms* from mineral
substances, using energy produced by chemical reactions.

CHLORINITY
See Salt content

CHROMOSOME
Complex linear structure of the cell nucleus containing DNA (deoxy-
ribonucleic acid) molecules.

CHRONOLOGICAL AGE
See Age

CITY
Generally large human settlement* under the jurisdiction of a munici-
pal government. Towns and villages generally also have a local government,* but are of smaller size and have more limited urban
resources. In some states of the United States, towns and townships
are territorial and political units similar to the communes in conti-
nental Europe.

CLIMATE
Prevailing weather conditions specific to an area over the long term.
Localized climate is referred to as microclimate, and climate of a
large region as macroclimate.

CLIMATIC REGION
See Climatic zone

CLIMATIC ZONE
Large region of generally homogeneous climate* delineated by lati-
tudes, mountains, bodies of water, and other land and atmospheric
factors. Syn.: Climatic region.

CLIMAX
See Biome

COASTAL ZONE
Strip of land of variable width along the shoreline, under the direct
environmental, economic, and social influences of the abutting body
of water. Syn.: Littoral zone.

COD TEST
See Chemical oxygen demand

COLLOID
Very fine particles (10 to 10,000 angstroms) of a substance dispersed
in suspension* in another substance, or dispersion medium. Can be
induced to settle by flocculants* or other means of precipitation.*

COLLUVIUM
Soil* particles, rocks, and debris deposited at the foot of cliffs and
slopes by gravity, wind, or surface runoff.*

COMFORT
Environmental conditions that produce a feeling of well-being.* The
ranges of these conditions (comfort zone or standard) vary among
individuals. Antonym: Discomfort.

COMFORT ZONE
See Comfort

COMMENSALISM
Relationship between organisms of two different species (ecological
interaction*) which is beneficial to one and indifferent to the other.

COMMODITY
See Good

COMMUNITY DESIGN
See Urban design

COMMUNITY FACILITY
Public or quasi-public building or installation, such as park, school,
or church, serving the cultural, recreational, civic, or religious
institutions of an urban community.*

COMMUNITY NOISE EQUIVALENT LEVEL
See Noise exposure forecast

COMMUNITY NOISE RATING
See Noise exposure forecast

COMMUNITY PARTICIPATION
Collective involvement of local citizens in the public affairs of their
community,* such as the early New England town meeting form of
local government. Citizens' participation in policy formulation and

decision making is formally or informally structured through public debates, development of local leadership, "advocacy planning," activist groups, pressure groups (or lobbies), neighborhood* councils, elected boards of special districts, and other forms of organization or control. Need for community participation is particularly felt in large developments where a single private firm determines policy, or at the neighborhood level of large cities* where governmental administration tends to be centralized, and representative democracy remote.

COMMUNITY PLAN
See Urban plan

COMPLEX TONE
Sound* containing simple sinusoidal components of different frequencies, which can be characterized in practice by its spectrum.*

COMPOST
Mixture of decaying organic material and refuse used to condition and fertilize the soil.* Can be produced from processed solid and liquid waste.*

COMPREHENSIVE PLAN
See Urban plan

CONCENTRATION
See Accumulation

CONGENITAL
Existing in an individual at birth, through heredity* or developed in the embryo during gestation.

CONSUMER
See Consumption (Economics); see Food chain (Ecology)

CONSUMER GOOD
See Good

CONSUMER SOCIETY
See Consumption

CONSUMPTION
Utilization or exhaustion of goods* in the satisfaction of wants* by the ultimate users, or consumers. A consumer society is characterized by an accelerated use of goods, caused by an increase in wants,

often artificially stimulated. This use tends to reduce capital formation and increase resources depletion, waste,* and the adverse effects
of waste disposal on the environment.*

CONTAGION
Transmission of a disease by direct or indirect contact.

CONTAMINANT
See Contamination

CONTAMINATION
Deposit, or action, of a pollutant,* or contaminant, on an organism
or a material surface. Pathological effects resulting from contact
with a contaminant. Generally limited to bacteria and radiation
exposure.*

CONURBATION (Brit.)
See Megalopolis

CORROSION
See Decomposition

COSMIC RADIATION
Ionizing radiation* of solar, galactic, or extragalactic origin.
Syn.: Cosmic rays.

COSMIC RAYS
See Cosmic radiation

COST-BENEFIT ANALYSIS
Technique used to determine the desirability and feasibility of a pro-
posed action (project or program), or to compare alternatives, by
identifying the costs and benefits associated with this action or actions,
and assigning monetary values to both. Many costs and benefits, especially of a social and environmental nature, do not lend themselves
to reliable quantifying, pricing, or forecasting, and are either ignored
or distorted in this analysis. Cost-effectiveness* analysis: Technique
used to evaluate the various means to achieve a specified objective,
by assessing the efficiency* of each operation and assigning monetary
values to all cost components, in order to minimize the cost for a
given effect, or maximize the effect at a given cost. Cost-effectiveness
analysis suffers to a lesser degree from defects similar to those of
cost-benefit analysis.

COST-EFFECTIVENESS ANALYSIS
See Cost-benefit analysis

COST OF LIVING
See Standard of living

CRITERION
Quantitative or qualitative data, such as environmental characteristics,
used as references for the testing or evaluation of suitability to certain
purposes or conformity to certain requirements. Used generally in
its plural form, criteria. Standard: Established degree of quality or
level of performance recognized as necessary to meet a certain
objective. Legal or regulatory standards are sanctioned by law or
administrative regulation.

CRITICAL
See Threshold

CROP ROTATION
Systematic cultivation of different successive crops on a parcel of
land, over a number of growing seasons, to reduce soil depletion,*
make more effective use of plant food, and control weeds, pests, and
diseases.

CRUDE BIRTH RATE
See Birth rate

CRUDE DEATH RATE
See Mortality rate

CULTURAL PRACTICES
See Pest control

CUMULATIVE EFFECT
See Accumulation

CURIE
See Radioactive series

DAM
Barrier, generally of earth, rock, and/or concrete, built across a
river valley to detain or divert and control the river's flow for a
single or multiple purpose such as water supply, navigation, recreation, power production, flood control, or irrigation.* As a result,
change in the regimen* of the river and creation of a reservoir* have
major effects on all aspects of the environment.*

DEATH RATE
See Mortality rate

DEATH RATE BY CAUSE OF DEATH
See Mortality rate

DECIBEL
One tenth of a bel; symbol DB; unit of measurement of sound-power
level* (and other quantities of power) expressing the ratio of two
values of power, equal to ten times the logarithm to the base ten of
this ratio.

DECOMPOSER
Heterotrophic* microorganism* capable of breaking down organic
matter into mineral compounds, thus providing a critical link in a
biogeochemical cycle.*

DECOMPOSITION
Molecular breakdown and change in composition of matter, particularly
organic matter, by chemical, physical, or organic agents. Corrosion:
Chemical or electrochemical decomposition of metals and alloys.
Chemical weathering: Chemical decomposition of rocks and minerals.
Air and water pollutants* can induce or accelerate these processes.

DECONTAMINATION FACTOR
See Radioactive decontamination

DEFOLIANT
Chemical substance that causes the premature loss of foliage when
applied to plants, primarily to facilitate agricultural processes such
as harvesting. Desiccants cause the drying up of foliage, with or
without accompanying falloff. Syn.: Drying agent. High risks of pollution of flora, fauna, and soils* are associated with the use of
defoliants and desiccants.

DEGREE OF ADAPTABILITY
See Adaptation

DEMAND SCHEDULE
See Market demand

DEMOGRAPHY
Field of science that deals with the quantitative characteristics,
geographic distribution, and evolution of human populations.*

DENATURATION
See Protein

DENITRIFICATION
See Nitrogen cycle

DESEGREGATION
See Social integration

DESICCANT
See Defoliant

DETACHED HOUSE
See House

DETERGENT
Cleansing substance containing surfactants* and other agents which
emulsify oil and hold dirt in suspension.* Some components of detergents are nonbiodegradable* and toxic, and produce persistent foam,
resistant to sewage treatment.

DEVELOPMENT PLAN
See Urban plan

DIETARY DEFICIENCY
Complete or partial lack of elements essential to nutrition,* occurring
in food,* diets, and living organisms.

DIETETICS
Field of science that deals with the principles of nutrition* and its
application, aiming at satisfying human nutritive needs under various
social, economic, age,* and health* conditions.

DIFFUSION
See Suspension

DIGESTED SLUDGE
See Sewage sludge

DISCHARGE
Emission* of liquid or solid substance. Also: Instantaneous rate of
flow of a fluid through a given section, expressed as volume per unit
of time. The phase of increasing discharge of a stream, or streamflow, is called rising stage; of decreasing discharge, falling stage;
of lowest discharge, lowest water level; of high discharge over the
banks, flood stage.

DISCOMFORT
See Comfort

DISINFECTANT
Chemical used to destroy pathogens* (but not bacterial spores), and
to treat the environment* to prevent their development.

DISPERSION
See Suspension

DISPERSION MEDIUM
See Colloid

DISPERSION MODEL
Mathematical prediction of the geographic concentration of air
pollutants* in an area, using specific hypothetical pollutant emission*
and meteorological conditions.

DNA MOLECULE
See Chromosome, Gene

DOMESTIC WASTE
See Liquid waste

DOMESTIC WATER
See Water supply

DOMINANCE
Manifestation of an inherited trait,* whether present in only one gene*
(heterozygous) or in both genes (homozygous) of the pair which determines such a trait (genetics). Commanding position of one or sometimes several animal or vegetal species in an ecosystem,* exerted
because of their greater abundance, their prevalence in ecological
interactions* with other species, or their monopolization of resources
such as sunlight, water, or food* (ecology).

DORMITORY SUBURB
See Suburb

DOSE EQUIVALENT
Measure of the effects of ionizing radiation* on exposed individual;
product of the specific absorbed dose* in rads* and modifying factors

(to take account of particular radiobiological characteristics); abbreviated: DE. Unit of measurement: rem (roentgen* equivalent in man). Dose equivalent rate: increase in dose equivalent during a period of time, per unit of time.

DOSE EQUIVALENT RATE
See Dose equivalent

DOSIMETER
Instrument that measures doses of ionizing radiation* received or absorbed.

DRAINAGE
Removal by pumping and/or gravity of excess water from the ground (subsurface drainage) to improve agricultural yield,* or disposal of surface runoff* or wetlands* water (surface drainage).

DRAINAGE BASIN
Area, bounded by a water divide, in which surface runoff* collects and is carried by streams and channels to a single outlet, such as river, lake,* or ocean. Syn.: Watershed, catchment area (Brit.).

DRINKING WATER
See Water supply

DROPLET
Fine liquid particle dispersed in suspension* in gases.

DRYING AGENT
See Defoliant

DUPLEX
See House

DUST SEPARATOR
Device for the removal of particulate matter* from a gas stream, by various techniques such as electrostatic precipitation,* scrubbing, screening, filtering, or centrifugal force.

DWELLING
Shelter designed and equipped for use as a home. Dwelling unit: Dwelling or self-contained part thereof used by a single household (family, individual, or small group with common housekeeping functions). Abbreviated: D.U. According to the number of D.U.s, a dwelling is designated as: single-family dwelling, two-family dwelling, or multifamily dwelling.

DWELLING UNIT
See Dwelling

ECOLOGICAL COMMUNITY
See Biocenose

ECOLOGICAL INTERACTION
Relation between individuals of the same species (intraspecific relation)
or of different species (interspecific relation) coexisting in a
biocenose.* This biodynamic interaction may be physiological or
behavioral, harmful, neutral, or beneficial to one or the other or both
individuals or species involved. Major forms of interactions are
mutualism,* commensalism,* neutralism, competition, parasitism,*
predation.* Syn.: Symbiosis.

ECOLOGICAL NICHE
Combination in one place of the environmental factors necessary to
support the particular life functions of an organism, a species, or a
population.* Also: Habitat* together with the system of interactions of
an organism, species, or population with its environment.*

ECOLOGICAL PYRAMID
Graphic representation of the trophic levels* in a food chain,* shown
as stacked horizontal bands with the producers* at the base, followed
by consumers* of the first, second, third order, and so on. Consumption* and transfers are expressed in terms of number of organisms
(number pyramid), amount of energy (energy pyramid), or quantity
of biomass* (biomass pyramid) at each trophic level.

ECOLOGY
Field of science that deals with the relationships between living
organisms and their environment, and among living organisms, with
reference to a single species under study (autecology), or to a group
of organisms such as a biocenose* (synecology).

ECONOMETRICS
Branch of economics* that deals with the measurement, analysis, and
projection of economic data, the development and testing of estimation, theories and models, using statistical and mathematical methods,
and computer technology.

ECONOMIC DEVELOPMENT
Rise in the economy of a country or region, through increased use of
energy and natural resources,* improvement of skill and management,
mechanization, application of new technology, and generally higher

capital investment and changes in the organization of the economic system. Economic development has a major impact on the society* and the environment* of an area.

ECONOMIC EXPANSION
Short-term increase in the capacity of an economic unit* to produce goods* and services.*

ECONOMIC GOOD
See Good

ECONOMIC GROWTH
Sustained increase in the production of goods* and services* in a country or region. Growth rate is measured by the percentage change during a given period, normally a year, of the real gross national product* (GNP adjusted for price changes). The real gross national product per capita is used for more meaningful indication of long-term changes.

ECONOMICS
Field of social science that deals with the activities a society engages in to provide for its needs. These activities include production, distribution, and consumption* of goods* and services,* and related aspects such as labor, income, money, taxation, trade, and natural resources.* Macroeconomics: Study of overall economic behavior, or of major sectors of the economy. Microeconomics: Study of the behavior of economic units* or of a limited sector of the economy.

ECONOMIC UNIT
Single agent of economic action at the lowest level of decision making. Depending on the type of economic analysis, it may be the individual, household,* group, firm, institution, or others.

ECOSYSTEM
Entity formed by the biotope* and the biocenose* naturally interacting as a single functional unit. (Contraction of "ecological system.")

ECOTONE
Transitional biotope* between two ecosystems,* such as tideland,* with intermediary environmental conditions constituting a new ecosystem, generally with a more diversified biocenose* than in either adjoining system, and more intense biological activity.

ECOTYPE
Sum of the inherited traits* of a population* group living in a given environment,* determined by selection,* isolation, and adaptation.*

By extension, group of individuals having the same ecotype-subunit of an ecospecies or taxonomic subspecies.

ECTOPARASITE
See Parasitism

EDAPHIC
Relation to the soil.*

EDAPHON
Totality of organisms living in the soil.*

EFFECTIVE DEMAND
See Market demand

EFFECTIVE HALF-LIFE
Average time interval necessary for half of a determined amount of nuclide* to undergo radioactive decay.*

EFFECTIVENESS
See Efficiency

EFFICIENCY
Relation between resources, such as labor, energy, time, capital, land, or raw material, utilized for production (factors of production), and the results achieved or goods* produced. Effectiveness: Degree to which specified objectives are achieved with given means and resources.

EFFLUENT
See Liquid waste

EMIGRATION
See Migration

EMISSION
Release of a solid, liquid, or gaseous substance, of radiations,* vibrations, heat, or other forms of energy, into a medium. Its origin is called source of emission, or sometimes source of pollution* when the emitted flux is a pollutant.* It can be concentrated (point source) or diffuse (nonpoint source), a stationary source or a mobile source. The term discharge* is commonly used for emission of liquid and solid substances.

EMULSION
See Suspension

ENDANGERED SPECIES
Wild animal or vegetal population* whose size is rapidly decreasing and whose survival is threatened by predation,* disease, and changes in ecological conditions, such as food shortage or disturbance of habitat.* Large numbers of species have become extinct, particularly in recent times from the effects of worldwide natural resource* and agricultural development, and population growth and dispersal. Endangered species can be preserved by wildlife protection measures.

ENDEMISM
Prevalence* and recurrence of a disease or other phenomena in a population* or a region (health). Presence of an animal or plant species confined to a certain region (ecology).

ENDOGENOUS
Originating within an organism, or caused by internal factors. Antonym: Exogenous.

ENDOPARASITE
See Parasitism

ENDOTOXIN
See Toxin

ENERGY PYRAMID
See Ecological pyramid

ENVIRONMENT
Sum of the physical, biotic,* and social factors and conditions directly or indirectly affecting the development, life, and activities of organisms and populations,* in the short and long term.

ENVIRONMENTAL HEALTH
Physical, biological, and social conditions in an environment* conducive to health.* By extension, measures and techniques used for the establishment, maintenance, and improvement of these conditions.

ENVIRONMENTAL INDICATOR
Quantified statement that describes the conditions of the environment* experienced by a population,* and their evolution. This statement is normally composed of an index or aggregate of indexes, expressed in relation to factors of exposure* and change over time. Factors of exposure include, in particular, the relative size or the type of population exposed to a condition, the geographic coverage, and length of time or frequency of exposure to this condition. Environmental indi-

cators are designed to monitor* and evaluate the quality of the environment and to project future conditions, to identify measures for improving this quality, and to assess the effectiveness of these measures. Social indicators, particularly housing indicators, are among the most widely used environmental indicators. An index of quality of an environmental component, such as air, is an instantaneous measurement of a critical parameter or datum, or of aggregated parameters or data, selected and weighted to reflect significant characteristics of this component and their relation to accepted thresholds.*

ENVIRONMENTAL NOISE
See Auditory environment

ENZYME
Type of protein* capable, under certain conditions, of acting as a catalyst in biochemical processes such as metabolism,* activating a chemical reaction in a cell without itself undergoing marked alteration or destruction in the process.

EPIDEMIC
Sudden abnormal increase in the incidence* of cases of an endemic* disease in a region, or rapid spreading of a contagious disease introduced in a population* or a region. By extension, rapid increase in the occurrence of other phenomena, such as accidents or suicides, in a population or a region.

EPIDEMIOLOGY
Field of science that deals with epidemic* diseases and other phenomena, and the physiological and environmental factors that determine their incidence,* frequency, distribution, and other characteristics.

EQUIVALENT SOUND LEVEL
See Sound level

EROSION
Loosening, removal, and transportation of soil* particles by wind action (wind erosion) or precipitation* and surface runoff.* Water erosion occurs as sheet erosion, or uniform surface action; rill erosion, in rivulets creating small trenches; or gully erosion, when deep trenches are formed. Frost, fire, overgrazing, land clearing, and other forms of plant-cover destruction can start or accelerate erosion.

ESTUARY
Place where a river empties into the open sea (river mouth) , forming a bay subject to tidal effects, where fresh water and sea water mix,

creating unique ecological conditions, and where development usually causes substantial pollution.*

ETHOLOGY
Field of science that deals with the behavior of animal species in their natural environments.*

EUTROPHIC
See Eutrophication

EUTROPHICATION
Process of modification of the physicochemical and biological characteristics of the water of lakes* and slow moving waterways, caused by an accumulation* of nutrients* from sewage effluents,* fertilizer*-laden runoff, and other sources, which increases the productivity and subsequent decay of aquatic organisms, especially phytoplankton,* and reduces the dissolved oxygen content. Eutrophication has undesirable effects on water quality, such as turbidity* or foul odor, and on ecosystems,* such as replacement of valuable fish species by less desirable ones. Eutrophic refers to a lake water habitat* at an advanced stage of eutrophication, rich in nutrients, poor in dissolved oxygen, and highly productive; mesotrophic refers to an intermediate stage of eutrophication, with moderate productivity; oligotrophic refers to an absence of eutrophication, poor in nutrients, rich in dissolved oxygen, and minimally productive.

EXOGENOUS
See Endogenous

EXOTOXIN
See Toxin

EXPOSURE
Condition in which an organism, object, or medium is subjected to the action of a pollutant* or other agent during a certain period (such as radiation exposure*).

EXPOSURE DOSE
See Radiation exposure

EXPRESSIVITY
Intensity of manifestation of an inherited trait* in an individual carrying it. Also, relative capacity of a gene* to manifest an inherited trait* in an individual. Expressivity depends upon the total genotype* and upon environmental factors.

EXTERNAL DISECONOMY
See Externality

EXTERNAL ECONOMY
See Externality

EXTERNALITY
Factor affecting the cost or benefit associated with an economic
activity, but outside the direct control or responsibility of the economic units* involved, and independent of the market mechanism. The
effect of this factor itself. External economy is a factor or effect
favorable to the economic units; external diseconomy is detrimental.
Not to be confused with social costs* and benefits. Used generally in
its plural form. Syn.: Spillover.

EXURB
See Suburb

FACTOR OF PRODUCTION
See Efficiency

FALLING STAGE
See Discharge

FALLOW LAND
Cultivated land left idle for one or more growing seasons in order to
restore the soil.*

FAMILY PLANNING
Deliberate control by a couple of the number of child births, or their
intervals, based on individual or societal considerations, through
various physiological, physical, or chemical means, such as contra-
ceptives, rhythm method, vasectomy, or sterilization.

FAST BREEDER REACTOR
Nuclear reactor* using highly enriched nuclear fuel* in the core, and
fertile material* in the "blanket." The process produces more
fissionable material,* such as plutonium, to produce heat and gener-
ate power than it consumes.

FATIGUE
Temporary reduction in the operational capacity of an organ or a
material system subjected to intensive or prolonged activity, stress,
or severe discomfort.* Often accompanied by pain for an individual
or weakening for a material, and leading eventually to exhaustion or
failure.

FECUNDITY
See Birth rate

FEEDSTUFF
See Foodstuff

FERMENT
See Fermentation

FERMENTATION
Transformation of organic matter, especially carbohydrates, by
anaerobic,* catalytic action of ferments, such as enzymes,* secreted
by microorganisms* such as yeast, molds, and bacteria. Process
used in particular for the production of alcohols, acids, cheese, and
bread.

FERTILE MATERIAL
Material, such as thorium 232 or uranium 238, capable of being converted into fissionable material* such as plutonium by capture of
neutrons.

FERTILITY
See Birth rate; also, Soil fertility

FERTILIZER
Organic or mineral substance which is incorporated into the soil* to
improve crop yield.* Production, misuse, and overuse of fertilizers
can cause land and water pollution, particularly eutrophication,* by
leaching* and runoff of nutrients* and other substances. These substances may also appear in abnormal concentration* in the harvested
plants (residual substances*).

FIELD CAPACITY
See Water holding capacity

FISSILE MATERIAL
See Fissionable material

FISSIONABLE MATERIAL
Material, such as uranium 235 or plutonium 239, whose nuclei are
capable of undergoing nuclear fission* by interaction with neutrons.
Syn.: Fissile material.

FLAVOR
Combined sensations of taste and smell.

FLOC
See Turbidity

FLOCCULANT
See Turbidity

FLOCCULATION
See Turbidity

FLOCCULE
See Turbidity

FLOOD STAGE
See Discharge

FLY ASH
Noncombustible particulate,* residues of combustion carried in the
combustion gases.

FOOD
Substance containing, or consisting of, nutrients,* which can be
ingested by a living organism to contribute to the maintenance of life
functions. Syn.: Nutriment.

FOOD ADDITIVE
Substance intentionally added to food* during processing, generally in
very small relative amounts, to improve its nutritional, physical, or
chemical properties (appearance, aroma, consistency, flavor*), or
its preservation capacity. Additives include preservatives, colorants,
emulsifiers, stabilizers, anti-oxidents, vitamins, and minerals, such
as iodide. Additives can be beneficial to health* such as iodide for
goiter prevention, or harmful such as sodium nitrite, believed to have
indirect carcinogenic effects.

FOOD CHAIN
Successive feeding of one organism on another in a constant and recur-
ring series, each feeding being referred to as trophic level, at which
phase matter or energy is transferred from a producer to a consumer
(animal or vegetal species) within an ecosystem.* Food* chains are
not strict linear series, but constitute an interdependent system
referred to as food web.

FOOD IRRADIATION
Treatment of foodstuff* by ionizing radiation* for preservation.

FOOD PRODUCT
See Foodstuff

FOODSTUFF
Raw or processed substance used for food by humans. Referred to as
food product when processed, and as feedstuff for animal consumption.

FOOD WEB
See Food chain

FOREST MANAGEMENT
Scientific and systematic utilization of forest resources, for maximum
production of timber on a sustained yield basis, by harvesting rotation
and cutting cycle, by reforestation, by disease, fire, and erosion*
control, and other forest practices; and for the preservation and
enhancement of the values of forests as watersheds,* wildlife
habitats,* and recreation and scenic areas. Forestry: Science that
deals with forest management.

FORESTRY
See Forest management

FREE GOOD
See Good

FREEZE DRYING
See Lyophilization

FUNGICIDE
See Pesticide

FUNGUS
Heterotrophic* thallophyte, such as yeast, mildew, mold, smut, and
mushroom, devoid of chlorophyl and living as parasite* or
saprophyte.*

FUTUROLOGY
Comprehensive multidisciplinary study of very long term evolution of
society* and its environment,* under the influence of changing attitudes and technological innovations.

GENE
Short segment of a DNA molecule, distributed in the chromosome*
according to a systematic and constant arrangement (genetic map),
and generally observable only at the time of cell division. The function

of each gene, acting in pairs on corresponding (or homologous) chromosomes is to determine a specific inherited trait* expressed through the production of a specific protein.*

GENE POOL
Sum of the genes* present among all the individuals of a population* or a species, transmitted from generation to generation.

GENERAL PLAN
See Urban plan

GENETIC DAMAGE
Deterioration of the quality of the inherited traits* present in a gene pool* or genetic inheritance.*

GENETIC INHERITANCE
Sum of the inherited traits* of an individual transmitted from ancestor to descendant.

GENETIC LOAD
Sum of the defective genes* carried in the gene pool* of a population* and producing defects, such as abnormalities, deformities, and physiological weaknesses, in every generation. Environmental factors may modify the natural selection* process or the rate of mutation,* which in turn may affect the genetic load.

GENETIC MAP
See Gene

GENETIC POLYMORPHISM
Coexistence of different genotypes* within a population.*

GENETICS
Field of science, derived from biology, that deals with the phenomena and mechanisms of hereditary transmission of biological traits and variations from that transmission.

GENETIC VARIATION
Difference of characteristics existing among individuals of the same population,* due to genotype* variations and differences in living conditions.

GENOTYPE
Genetic constitution of an individual. By extension, group of individuals having the same genetic constitution.

GERMINAL
See Somatic

GHETTO
See Slum

GOOD
Material of any sort having a value to individuals and society,* with
distinct meanings in terms such as economic or free good, social,
capital, or consumer good. Generally used in its plural form in
economics.* Economic good: Product from agriculture, mining, or
manufacturing with a market value in a monetary economy, derived
from being wanted, relatively scarce, and transferable. Services*
are included as part of goods; the expression "goods and services"
is used to distinguish the material and nonmaterial aspects of the
term "goods." Syn.: Commodity. Free good: Good available in
abundance at no economic cost at the point where it is wanted. If
transportable, it becomes an economic good after transportation.
Economic growth tends to cause a shift of free goods, such as fresh
air, clean water, or scenery, to economic goods by reduction of
their quality or quantity. Syn.: Nonmonetary commodity. Social good:
Good which has a higher value to society* in general than to any single
economic unit,* and whose market price* is therefore difficult to
estimate. Capital good: Economic good such as equipment, structure,
or raw material inventory, used for the production of other goods.
Land and money technically are not included. Consumer good: Durable
or nondurable economic good used directly by consumers for the
satisfaction of their own wants. Depending on the type of economic
analysis, long-lived durable goods such as cars and houses are
treated as consumer goods or capital goods.

GRAVITATIONAL WATER
See Water-holding capacity

GREEN BELT
See Open space

GROSS NATIONAL PRODUCT
Total monetary value of all final goods* and services* produced in a
country during a given period, normally a year, at current prices.
Abbreviated: GNP. Net national product is the gross national product
less consumption of capital, or depreciation. These aggregate measures of the economy of a country do not include, however, nonmarket
values, such as a housewife's work, or social costs,* such as pollution or depletion of exhaustible resources.

GROUND-LEVEL CONCENTRATION
Proportional amount of pollutants* contained in the air measured in
parts per million (ppm) or micrograms per cubic meter ($\mu g/m^3$) between the ground level and the height of man.

GROUNDWATER
Subsurface water below the water table retained in aquifers* and
cavities of the earth. Groundwater containing minerals or gases
(mineral water) may be undesirable for domestic or industrial uses,
or desirable for medical purposes.

GROUP BEHAVIOR
See Social behavior

GULLY EROSION
See Erosion

GUSTATORY RECEPTOR
See Savor

HABITAT
Space used for human domestic activities. Local environmental
conditions, current technology, and life style* of the community*
largely determine the design and construction of a habitat (Human
settlements). Particular environment* in which lives an organism,
or a group or community of organisms (Ecology).

HALOGEN
Constituent of trace elements (chlorine, iodine, bromide, fluorine,
and astatine) present in the atmosphere in aerosol* form, originating
from natural sources such as sea water, and human sources such as
fuel combustion, causing air pollution.*

HEALTH
Condition exhibited by an individual free from disease or organic
disability, and in full possession of his physical and mental faculties;
demonstrating a reasonable resistance to pathogens,* allergens,*
and toxicants, and maintaining a state of equilibrium with his environment. More specifically identified as physical health and mental health.

HEARING LEVEL
Amount by which the threshold of audibility* of one ear exceeeds a
prescribed standard audiometric threshold, used to measure impair-
ment of hearing. Syn.: Hearing threshold level, hearing loss.

HEARING LOSS
See Hearing level

HEARING THRESHOLD LEVEL
See Hearing level

HERBICIDE
See Pesticide

HEREDITY
Process of genetic transmission of characteristics from ancestor to
descendant. By extension, genetic inheritance.*

HERTZ
See Audio frequency

HETEROTROPH
Organism that feeds on organic matter. Saprophyte: Vegetal organism
feeding on decaying organic matter. Saprozoic: Feeding on decaying
organic matter; applied to animals.

HETEROZYGOUS
See Dominance (Genetics)

HOMOZYGOUS
See Dominance, Recessive

HOST
See Parasitism

HOUSE
Building used for human habitation. Further designated as detached
house, semidetached house (or duplex), row house, town house, or
apartment house (or residential building), according to the form and
size of the building.

HOUSEHOLD
See Dwelling

HOUSING DENSITY
See Population density

HOUSING REHABILITATION
Restoration or improvement of deteriorated residential buildings
through repair, redecorating, remodeling (generally short of

structural alteration), or installation of new plumbing, wiring, insulation, equipment, landscaping, and other improvements. Undertaken by resident owner, private investor, local public agency, or nonprofit organization, sometimes with public financial aid.

HUMAN SETTLEMENT
Place ranging in size from village* to metropolis,* where population* is concentrated for habitation and employment, and where public and commercial services, and cultural, religious, and civic institutions are available.

HUMIFICATION
See Humus

HUMUS
Dark-colored organic portion of the soil*; well-decomposed material of vegetal and animal origin. Humification: Process of transformation of organic material into humus.

HYDROGEOLOGY
Field of science that deals with the underground part of the hydrosphere* and with the effects of water on the surface of the earth.

HYDROLOGIC CYCLE
Continuous circulation of the water of the earth through successive phases including precipitation,* runoff, infiltration, storage, and evapotranspiration, which are repeated upon completion. Syn.: Water cycle.

HYDROLOGY
Field of science that deals with the hydrosphere,* and particularly with the water resources of the land areas of the earth.

HYDROPONICS
See Aquiculture

HYDROSPHERE
Combined parts of water present on the earth (surface water*), in the atmosphere* (water vapor), and in the lithosphere* (groundwater*).

HYGIENE
Field of science that deals with the principles, methods, and practices aimed at the preservation and improvement of health.* It has many aspects: personal hygiene, domestic hygiene, community hygiene, industrial hygiene, and mental hygiene.

IMMIGRATION
See Migration

IMMUNITY
See Allergy

IMPURITY
Foreign matter present in small amounts in a substance, which
reduces its quality. Called adulterant when added to a substance.

INCIDENCE
See Morbidity rate

INDEX OF QUALITY
See Environmental indicator

INDIGENOUS
Originating naturally and living in a particular region or biotope.*
Syn.: Native, autochthonous.

INDUCED RADIOACTIVITY
Radioactivity* created in a substance by exposure* to ionized radiation*
from radioactive decay.*

INDUSTRIAL WASTE WATER
See Liquid waste

INDUSTRIAL WATER
See Water supply

INFANT MORTALITY RATE
See Mortality rate

INFECTION
Penetration into a living body of a microorganism,* generally a
pathogen.* Condition resulting from this penetration.

INFESTATION
See Pest

INFRASONIC VIBRATION
Vibration whose frequency is below the audio frequency* range (under
15 cycles per second, or hertzes) and therefore not audible by man.
Infrasonic vibrations can nevertheless produce disturbing effects that
can be felt at great distances. Infrasonic is not to be confused with
subsonic which refers to speeds lower than the speed of sound.*

INHERITED TRAIT
Physical, physiological, expressed, or latent character or characteristic genetically transmitted to an individual by a parent, independently of any environmental influence.

INSECTICIDE
See Pesticide

INTEGRATED CONTROL
See Pest control

INTERSPECIFIC RELATION
See Ecological interaction

INTERTIDAL ZONE
See Tideland

INTRASPECIFIC RELATION
See Ecological interaction

IONIZING RADIATION
Particles such as electrons, charged with sufficient energy to produce ionization directly upon passage through a substance. Particles not energetically charged, such as neutrons, capable of releasing ionizing particles or of inducing nuclear reaction.*

IRRADIATION
Intentional exposure* to a radiation,* in particular an ionizing radiation.*

IRRIGATION
Watering of arable land by pumping and/or gravity, to compensate for a lack or shortage of rainfall* in certain areas and/or at certain periods, in order to place new land in cultivation, introduce new crops, or increase the yield* of existing ones. Irrigation generally has major effects on the environment,* and often produces crops of lesser flavor, lower nutritional value, and other characteristics.

IRRIGATION WATER
See Water supply

LAKE
Inland body of water resulting from natural or man-made blockage of river and surface runoff* water outflow. Slow water replenishment

rate causes cumulative and long-lasting pollution* phenomena such as eutrophication.* Absence of outlet, low rainfall,* and high evaporation result in high salinity of lake water. Man-made lakes are generally referred to as <u>reservoirs</u>.

LAND CLEARING
Destruction of natural vegetation over areas intended for cultivation, causing changes in their ecological and biological balances.

LAND RECLAMATION
Management practices utilized to recover and restore scarred and other land, such as marshy or strip-mined land or spoil heap,* unsuited for agricultural and other economically productive uses.

LAND SUBSIDENCE
Lowering or collapsing of the ground surface resulting from mining; withdrawal of fluids such as groundwater,* oil, and natural gas, by pumping, drainage,* or evaporation; compaction of plastic or elastic soil,* or soil with a large water content; or formation of porous or cavernous soil by dissolution of carbonate rock. Construction on land subject to subsidence can result in serious damage.

LAND USE DENSITY
See Population density

LATERITE
Usually reddish soil,* rich in oxides of metals such as aluminum, titanium, manganese, and especially iron, found particularly in damp, tropical regions, which hardens on exposure* to the atmosphere* and forms a rocky crust. <u>Laterization</u>: Evolution of a soil to laterite by weathering, under the influence of hot, humid climate* and/or destruction of the forest or savanna by fire or clearing, causing the removal of silica and alkalies, and an increase in concentration* of iron and aluminum oxides.

LATERIZATION
See Laterite

LEACHING
Dissolution and removal of soluble constituents of the soil,* mostly salts, by seepage of water through the soil (<u>percolation</u>), resulting in desirable or undesirable effects on its fertility* and on the ecosystem.*

LENITIC
See Lentic

LENTIC
Pertaining to standing water, such as in lakes* and ponds. Antonym: Lotic, pertaining to swiftly moving water. Syn.: Lenitic.

LIFE EXPECTANCY
Statistical probability of duration of life of individuals, based on age-specific death rates,* varying for different populations,* population categories,* and groups, and affected by genetic and environmental factors.

LIFE STYLE
See Standard of living

LIMNETIC
See Pelagic

LIMNOLOGY
Science that deals with lakes* and rivers, and their environmental phenomena and processes.

LIQUID WASTE
Water rejected after usage in communities (domestic waste), industry (industrial waste water), agriculture, and so on, which is micro-biologically, chemically, and/or physically polluted. Called raw sewage when collected in sewers, and treated sewage or effluent after processing in a treatment plant. Syn.: Waste water.

LITHOSPHERE
Solid outer layer of the earth, approximately 100 km. thick, above the mantle and under the atmosphere* and hydrosphere.* Comprised of a lighter upper part, the sial, in which silicon and aluminum (in particular, granite) are dominant, and a heavier lower part, the sima, in which silicon and magnesia (in particular, basalt) are dominant.

LITTER
Upper layer of dead organic material, at an early stage of decay, covering the forest floor. Called mulch when spread on soil for agri-cultural purposes. Also: Waste* or refuse material, such as paper or used containers, discarded on the ground. Scattered litter can be a significant pollutant* of the urban and rural landscape.

LITTORAL ZONE
See Coastal zone

LOCAL GOVERNMENT
General-purpose political and administrative unit below the federal and state levels, whose authority derives from the state government. Includes counties and municipalities and their equivalents (parishes, townships, towns,* and villages*), and excludes regional and district organizations.

LOTIC
See Lentic

LOWEST WATER LEVEL
See Discharge

LYOPHILIZATION
Dehydration by rapid freezing at very low temperature, of a material to be preserved (such as food* or blood), followed by rapid sublimation in a high vacuum. Syn.: Freeze drying.

MACROCLIMATE
See Climate

MACROECONOMICS
See Economics

MALNUTRITION
Inadequate nutrition* due to under- or overnourishment, imbalanced diet, defective digestion or assimilation,* or other causes.

MARINE SCIENCES
See Oceanography

MARKET DEMAND
Want,* willingness, and ability of individuals to acquire an economic good* at a given price, or market price, as determined by prevailing demand and supply conditions at a particular time. By extension, the amount of a specific good that buyers stand ready to acquire at a certain price level, or demand schedule. Syn.: Effective demand.

MARKET PRICE
See Market demand

MARSH
See Wetlands

MASKED SOUND
See Masking

MASKING
Rise in the threshold of audibility* for a given sound (masked sound) due to the presence of another (masking sound), generally expressed in decibels.*

MASKING SOUND
See Masking

MASTER PLAN
See Urban plan

MECHANICAL VIBRATION
Continuing periodic motion of parts of machines or structures, generally unintentional and having undesirable effects.

MEGALOPOLIS
Region formed by the gradual merging of neighboring cities* and metropolises* by urbanization* of the intervening rural land. Syn.: Conurbation (Brit.).

MENTAL AGE
See Age

MENTAL HEALTH
See Health

MESOTROPHIC
See Eutrophication

METABOLIC RATE
See Metabolism

METABOLISM
Physical and chemical processes of transformation of food* by an organism, and its utilization for the maintenance of life functions. Metabolic rate: Ability of a given organism, species, or population to produce organic matter or energy by synthesis, measured in relation to units of time and biomass.* Subject to variations due to environmental conditions such as temperature.

METEOROLOGY
Field of science that deals with the atmosphere,* its properties and phenomena, in particular weather. Atmospheric sciences refer to the various distinct sciences that are applied to the study of the atmosphere.

METROPOLIS
Major urban center of trade, industry and/or government for a region
or nation. Metropolitan area is the urbanized area* of a metropolis.

METROPOLITAN AREA
See Metropolis

MICROCLIMATE
See Climate

MICROECONOMICS
See Economics

MICRONUTRIENT
Trace element, or organic compound such as vitamin, necessary to
organisms in minute amounts for the maintenance of life functions,
particularly as a catalytic agent. Trace element: Element or chemical
compound occurring in minute amounts in the environment* and in
organisms.

MICROORGANISM
Organism, such as bacterium, protozoan, virus, and some algae*
and fungi,* of microscopic or ultramicroscopic dimension.

MIGRATION
Movement of individuals, families, or groups from one place of
residence to another, under the effects of economic, social, political,
or environmental factors, considered from the point of origin
(emigration) or destination (immigration). Major characteristics of
migration are the distance, area (city, region, or nation), and type
(rural or urban) of the origin and destination, and duration (seasonal
or permanent).

MINERAL WATER
See Groundwater

MIXED LAYER
See Surface water

MOBILE SOURCE
See Emission

MODEL
Physical or abstract representation or simulation of an existing,
planned, or foreseen situation or activity, designed to facilitate its

analysis, test a hypothesis, or predict a behavior. Used in environmental studies, such as air pollution (dispersion model*).

MOLLUSCICIDE
See Pesticide

MONITORING
Process of observation, measurement, recording, and/or evaluation, over a continuous period of time, generally at specific intervals, of the evolution of a phenomenon or condition, in order to ascertain conformity to certain objectives and take corrective action when indicated. Now largely accomplished with the assistance of devices such as sensors, probes, photography, films, radio and telecommunication, and space satellites.

MORBIDITY RATE
Ratio of individuals having contracted a disease to the total population,* expressed in terms of either the prevalence of cases at a given time, or the incidence of new cases during a given period.

MORTALITY RATE
Ratio of death to population* during a given period in a specified area. Generally expressed as crude death rate (number of deaths per thousand population per year). More meaningful indexes of mortality are: age-specific death rate (number of deaths per 100,000 population of a given age group such as infant mortality rate), death rate by cause of death (number of deaths from a given disease or other cause per 100,000 population), or case fatality rate (number of deaths due to a disease per thousand population having contracted this disease). Syn.: Death rate.

MOUTH OF A RIVER
See Estuary

MULCH
See Litter

MULTIFAMILY DWELLING
See Dwelling

MUTAGEN
Physical or chemical agent, such as heat, radioactive element,* ultraviolet radiation, or nitric acid, capable of inducing mutation* by altering the structure of the DNA molecule.*

MUTANT
Individual bearing a gene* that has undergone a mutation* that is observable (expressed in the phenotype*).

MUTATION
Sudden alteration in a gene* or genotype* of an individual; rare and unpredictable, and inheritable when occurring in a germ cell. The mutation rate expresses the probability of occurrence of mutation of a gene during the lifetime of an individual. Spontaneous mutations occur generally at a rate of less than one in a hundred thousand.

MUTATION RATE
See Mutation

MUTUALISM
See Synergism

MYCOTOXIN
See Toxin

NATIONAL INCOME
Total monetary value of the earnings of all people and economic units* of a country from the production of all goods* and services* during a given period, normally a year.

NATIVE
See Indigenous

NATURALIZATION
See Acclimatation

NATURAL RADIATION
Ionizing radiation* from naturally radioactive elements.

NATURAL RADIOACTIVITY
Radioactivity* of natural radionuclides.*

NATURAL RESOURCE
Mineral or biotic element, or form of energy, occurring in its natural state in the environment,* considered from the standpoint of its potential or realized value to society.* Natural resources are referred to as: renewable, such as timber or fish, through biological production,* or such as water or nitrogen, through the biogeochemical cycle* process; nonrenewable, or exhaustible, such as mineral deposits; or permanent, such as solar, tidal, or eolian energy. Natural resource

management: Utilization of natural resources in a manner that mini-
mizes depletion, waste, and environmental damage or pollution,
allows for their renewal or recovery, and maximizes quality and
productivity,* for all desirable purposes, to the greatest benefit of
society over the long term. This management applies in particular
to air, water, soil,* minerals, forest, and wildlife.

NATURAL RESOURCE MANAGEMENT
See Natural resource

NATURAL SELECTION
Genetic process in which environmental factors favor or induce the
survival and propagation of a particular genotype* over others in a
population.* Major determinant of the genetic polymorphism* of a
population through elimination of genetic variation* introduced by
mutation* and migration.*

NATURE PRESERVE
Area containing distinctive natural plant and animal communities*
set aside, generally by government action, for recreational, educational, and scientific use.

NEIGHBORHOOD
Geographic subarea of the city,* generally residential, with its own
specific character, community facilities,* such as elementary school,
shopping center, fire station, church, and movie theater, its own
social entity derived from its common institutions and sometimes
ethnic background, and, in some cities, its own administrative unit
such as a precinct. Structurally formalized in urban planning* as
neighborhood unit.

NEIGHBORHOOD CONSERVATION
See Urban renewal

NEIGHBORHOOD UNIT
See Neighborhood

NEMATOCIDE
See Pesticide

NET NATIONAL PRODUCT
See Gross national product

NET REPRODUCTION RATE
See Birth rate

NITRIFICATION
See Nitrogen cycle

NITROGEN CYCLE
Biogeochemical cycle* of the element nitrogen through the soil,* organisms, and the atmosphere* (as nitrogen gas) by a succession of transformation processes—in particular: Nitrogen fixation: Transformation of nitrogen gas from the atmosphere into nitrate ions assimilable by plants, by certain algae* and bacteria, mostly rhizobia living symbiotically in leguminous plant root nodules; Ammonification: Generally aerobic* transformation by microorganisms* of nitrogenous organic substance into ammonia; Nitrification: Oxidation of ammonia by microorganisms, producing nitrite, then nitrate, assimilable by plants; Denitrification: Reduction of nitrate to nitrite, ammonia, and nitrogen gas by microorganisms in soil or water.

NITROGEN FIXATION
See Nitrogen cycle

NOISE
Any unwanted sound* that generally interferes with the perception of other sounds and has unpleasant, annoying, or traumatizing effects. By extension, unwanted disturbance due to an erratic or intermittent oscillation such as in electrical transmission.

NOISE EXPOSURE FORECAST (NEF)
Combined single measurement unit of community exposure to aircraft noise, based on modified perceived noise level,* taking into account the number of flights over given day and night periods. Abbreviated: NEF. NEF contours plotted on a map indicate the points of equal noise exposure from runways and flight paths. Community noise rating (CNR) and community noise equivalent level (CNEL) are variations of this measurement.

NONMONETARY COMMODITY
See Good

NONPOINT SOURCE
See Emission

NONRENEWABLE RESOURCE
See Natural resource

NUCLEAR ENERGY
Energy released by nuclear reaction.*

NUCLEAR FISSION
Nuclear reaction* in which heavy nuclei split in two parts with simultaneous release of energy.

NUCLEAR FUEL
Fissionable* or fertile* material with a reasonably long effective radioactive half-life* used as a source of energy in a nuclear reactor.*

NUCLEAR FUSION
Nuclear reaction* in which light nuclei combine to form heavier nuclei with simultaneous release of energy. A thermonuclear fusion is a fusion produced at very high temperatures.

NUCLEAR PILE
See Nuclear reactor

NUCLEAR REACTION
Process such as nuclear fission,* fusion,* or radioactive decay,* which alters the energy, composition, or structure of an atomic nucleus.

NUCLEAR REACTOR
Device used to initiate and maintain a controlled chain nuclear reaction,* consuming fissionable material* and producing heat used for power generation, and neutrons and fission products for experimental and medical purposes. Obsolete syn.: Atomic pile, atomic reactor, nuclear pile

NUCLIDE
Atom characterized by the structure of its nucleus (protons and neutrons) and its energy content. A radionuclide is a nuclide that exhibits radioactivity.*

NUMBER PYRAMID
See Ecological pyramid

NUTRIENT
Organic or inorganic substance including protein,* fat, carbohydrate, vitamins, and minerals, constituting the nutritive element of food* used by a living organism through assimilation* for heat or energy, growth or restoration, and physiological processes (hormonal, enzymic, and so on).

NUTRITION
Utilization of food* by an organism to maintain life functions through digestion, assimilation,* separation, elimination, and other complex physiological processes.

OCEANOGRAPHY
Field of science that deals with the ocean, its properties and phenomena. Oceanology is occasionally used, with some variation of meaning
or as a synonym. Marine sciences refer to the various distinct sciences that are applied to the study of the oceans, such as marine
biology or zoology.

OCEANOLOGY
See Oceanography

OIL DUMPING
See Oil pollution

OIL POLLUTION
Pollution* of the ocean, and occasionally lakes* and rivers, by dis-
charge* of hydrocarbons, mostly petroleum crude oil, during trans-
portation or storage, from tanks, tankers, or pipelines. Oil spill:
Accidental discharge, usually as a result of storm or collision.
Oil dumping: Intentional discharge, primarily from tanker-hold
flushing. Oil slick: Generally small discharge on the water surface.
Black tide: Substantial deposit on tidelands* from oil spill or dumping.

OIL SLICK
See Oil pollution

OIL SPILL
See Oil pollution

OLIGOTROPHIC
See Eutrophication

OPEN SPACE
Land predominantly free of buildings, in an urban region. Sometimes
protected from development by government action to provide for out-
door recreation, to preserve prime agricultural land, wooded areas,
exceptional views, and land or water features, and to channel urban
growth. It excludes land used for transportation such as trafficways,
railroads, or parking lots. Buffer zone: Open space strip with tree
and plant cover. Set aside and maintained to provide a separation
between two different types of land use, and to reduce objectionable
effects of one on the other. Syn.: Buffer strip. Green belt: Area of
parks, woods, and farmland set aside and maintained generally by
government action around a city,* to contain urban expansion, to
prevent urban sprawl beyond the city and the establishment of undesirable uses on its immediate periphery, and to provide directly acces-
sible countryside and recreation areas to city dwellers.

ORGANIC FARMING
Cultivation practices emphasizing natural and organic methods and substances, in reaction to industrialized agriculture and excessive use of chemical fertilizers,* pesticides,* and other mineral and synthetic materials.

OVICIDE
See Pesticide

OZONE LAYER
See Aerosol propellant

PARASITE
See Parasitism

PARASITISM
Association between two organisms of different kinds (ecological interaction*), beneficial (food* and shelter) to one (parasite) and harmful to the other (host). Ectoparasites carry out the infestation* by external attachment to the host; endoparasites by internal penetration.

PARTICLE DETECTOR
Device, generally used together with a metering instrument, to indicate the presence of ionizing radiation.* Syn.: Radiation detector.

PARTICLE VELOCITY
Instantaneous speed of a given infinitesimal part of a medium under the action of a sound* wave, with reference to this medium.

PARTICULATE MATTER
See Particulate

PARTICULATE
Fine solid particle of various origins dispersed in suspension* in gases and smoke. Collectively referred to as particulate matter.

PATHOGEN
Disease-producing agent, usually a living microorganism.*

PEAK CONCENTRATION
See Accumulation

PEDOGENESIS
See Soil genesis

PEDOLOGY
See Soil science

PELAGIC
Pertaining to the environment* of the open sea; capable of sustained
life away from and independent of the littoral and the ocean floor.
When applied to a fresh water body: Limnetic.

PENETRANCE
Probability of frequency of manifestation of an inherited trait* in an
individual carrying it. Penetrance depends upon the total genotype*
and upon environmental factors.

PERCEIVED NOISE LEVEL
Rating of annoyance due to aircraft noise based on sound-level* measurement, adjusted for tone spectrum and frequency band, and taking
account of single noise duration. Abbreviated: PNL.

PERCOLATION
See Leaching

PERMANENT RESOURCE
See Natural resource

PERSISTENCE
Retention by certain pollutants* of their toxic strength for periods
varying from hours, for some bacteria, to thousands of years, for
radioactive material;* their resistance to biodegradation,* dilution,
removal, or elimination by the organism; and their transfer from
one organism to another through trophic levels.*

PEST
Organism visible to the naked eye, or animal and vegetal species
considered detrimental to specific human activities or objectives at
a given place and time, such as certain insects, rodents, or
predators.* Infestation: Presence in one place of large quantities of
pests. Also: Attachment of a parasite* on or in a host.*

PEST CONTROL
Use of techniques aimed at the destruction of pests,* or at inhibiting
their growth and reproduction. Chemical control techniques rely on
the use of pesticides*; physical control, use of physical agents such
as temperature, humidity, electric shock, radioactivity*; biological
control, use of biological means such as parasites,* predators, or
sterile males (through chemical or radiation* sterilization); cultural

<u>practices</u>, use of resistant varieties of crops, selected seeds or fertilizers, weed control, crop rotation, or other agronomic measures for the protection of crops against pests; <u>integrated control</u>, use of a compatible combination of several of these control techniques.

PESTICIDE
Chemical compound applied to plants, soil,* seed, water, food,* or other contact points, for pest control* purposes. Derived from mineral substances such as sulfur or copper, extracted from organic substances such as nicotine or pyrethrum, or synthesized from organic substances such as dichlorodiphenyltrichloroethane (DDT). Pesticides are named according to their control purposes, such as <u>insecticide</u>, <u>herbicide</u>, <u>fungicide</u>, <u>nematocide</u>, <u>rodenticide</u>, <u>algicide</u>, <u>bactericide</u>, <u>molluscicide</u>, <u>ovicide</u>, and <u>virucide</u>. The toxicity, mobility, persistence,* and cumulative effect* of certain pesticides result in damage to other than the target species, beyond the area of application, and after the period of application. Syn.: <u>Biocide</u>.

PHENOTYPE
Sum of the observable characteristics of an individual produced by the genotype* under the influence of environmental factors. By extension, group of individuals exhibiting the same phenotype.

PHOTOCHEMICAL SMOG
See Smog

PHOTOSYNTHESIS
Synthesis of organic substances by chlorophyl-containing plants from mineral substances, using chemical energy converted from light energy.

PHYSICAL CONTROL
See Pest control

PHYSICAL HEALTH
See Health

PHYTOGEOGRAPHY
See Biogeography

PHYTOPLANKTON
See Plankton

PHYTOTOXIN
See Toxin

PLANKTER
See Plankton

PLANKTON
Any of many classes of vegetal (phytoplankton) and animal (zooplankton) organisms, mostly unicellular and microscopic, living in suspension in bodies of fresh or sea water, moved by currents or weakly motile. Occurrence and reproduction of plankton are highly dependent on environmental factors such as chemical composition, particularly salinity and phosphate concentration, depth, light, temperature, and speed of currents. Plankter: Single organism of plankton. Phytoplankton performs major functions of atmospheric oxygen fixation, and of protein* storage and renewal basic to the food chain.* Its proliferation in stagnant water can seriously reduce water quality (eutrophication*).

PLANNING
Management process consisting of formulating policies, defining objectives pursuant to these policies, and developing programs with short- and long-term schedules for the implementation of these objectives. Further defined by its primary user, such as corporate planning, public planning; its geographic coverage such as neighborhood* planning, urban planning,* regional planning*; or its functional coverage, such as transportation planning, land-use planning, school planning, economic planning, or comprehensive planning.

PLANT ASSOCIATION
See Biocenose

PLANT COMMUNITY
See Biocenose

PLURALISTIC SOCIETY
Harmonious coexistence in one society* of diverse and distinct ethnic, religious, political, or cultural groups and value systems. Concept derived from philosophical pluralism and from doctrines of individual freedom and equality, stressing group identity, tradition, and even autonomy, sometimes in conflict with the concept of assimilation and conformist attitude.

PODZOL
Greyish-white bleached soil* of high acidity due to the leaching* of alkalic compounds toward its lower layers. Its surface layer generally consists of organic matting. Develops in moist and cool climates, and especially under coniferous forests. Podzolization: Evolution of a soil toward a podzol type under the action of acidification factors such as litter* formation and acid precipitation.

PODZOLIZATION
See Podzol

POINT SOURCE
See Emission

POLLUTANT
Physical, chemical, or biological substance, material, or agent,
generally resulting from human activities, which reduces certain
qualities of the environment* in which it is introduced, and/or the
well-being* of the organisms exposed to it. Pollution: Emission* of
pollutants into the environment, or results of this emission.

POLLUTION
See Pollutant

POPULATION
Sum of all inhabitants of a specific area at a given period (demography). Group of organisms of a biome* sharing a common gene pool*
(ecology).

POPULATION CATEGORY
See Population composition

POPULATION COMPOSITION
Division of the population* into categories constituting discrete,
measurable qualities of the individuals of this population, such as:
age*, sex, family status, physical and mental traits and health, ethnic
origin, language, religion, education, income, occupation and skill,
or place of birth or residence. These categories are subdivided into
population groups with a single common characteristic, for general
or specific description and analysis. A common graphic representation of population composition is the population pyramid showing with
horizontal histograms, or bar chart, the frequency distribution of the
population in each age interval by sex.

POPULATION DENSITY
Measure of the distribution and intensity of settlement of population*
on land, expressed in average number of persons, families, or
dwelling units* per area unit, such as acre or square mile. Land use
density: Ratio of the total floor area of buildings to area of ground
(FAR), or ratio of coverage of ground by buildings. Housing density:
Measure of the intensity of occupancy of dwellings,* expressed in
number of persons per room, or amount of usable floor space per
dwelling unit.* Density issues, such as population concentration or

dispersal, overpopulation and overcrowding, are major factors of environmental quality.

POPULATION DYNAMICS
Process of evolution and mutation in the size, composition, and geographic distribution of a population* under genetic, environmental, and social influences.

POPULATION GENETICS
Theoretical, empirical, and experimental study of the current state and evolution of genetic polymorphism* of a population.* Environmental factors, in particular, determine the parameters that describe this polymorphism.

POPULATION MOBILITY
Ability and tendency of individuals, families, or groups to change their places of residence. The movement itself, expressed in rate of frequency, distance, and number of people, during a given period (in the United States, currently, once every five years on the average, for the entire population).

POPULATION PYRAMID
See Population composition

PRECINCT
See Neighborhood

PRECIPITATION
Water vapor of the atmosphere* falling to earth after condensation, in the form of rain, snow, sleet, hail, or mist. Phase of the hydrologic cycle.* By extension, amount expressed in depth of liquid water at a given point over a specified period (rainfall*). Also: See Suspension.

PREDATION
Ecological interaction* process of hunting, killing, and eating of an animal of one species (prey) by an animal of another species (predator). Predation exists also in some plants, such as the Venus flytrap.

PREDATOR
See Predation

PREVALENCE
See Morbidity rate

PREVENTIVE MEDICINE
Study and application of medical means to prevent or reduce the occurrence of diseases and disabilities, and to maintain environmental health. Prophylaxis: Methods and measures to prevent the occurrence or spread of diseases, and to maintain health.*

PREY
See Predation

PRICE INDEX
See Purchasing power

PRIMARY PRODUCTION
See Biological production

PRIMARY STAGE
See Biological cycle

PRIMITIVE AREA
See Wilderness area

PRODUCER
See Food chain

PRODUCTIVITY
Form of efficiency* measurement expressed as the ratio between the quantity of certain factors of production* required (input), and the quantity of goods* of specified quality produced (output), using monetary or physical units. Can be expressed variously as agricultural products per acre, manufactured goods per labor over time, or percent return for capital invested.

PROPHYLAXIS
See Preventive medicine

PROTEIN
Nitrogenous molecule consisting of a chain of amino acids whose specific type, combination, and linkage give the molecule its characteristics. Present in all living cells and essential for the growth and repair of tissues. Obtained by plants from mineral substances through photosynthesis,* and assimilated by animals. All proteins are susceptible to irreversible molecular structure changes, called denaturation, under the influence of certain agents such as chemicals, heat, or radiation.*

PUBLIC HEALTH
Conditions of health* of the individuals of a community. Measures
and techniques used to achieve these conditions, under governmental
supervision.

PURCHASING POWER
Ability of individuals to acquire wanted and needed goods,* contingent
on their disposable personal income and the market prices* of these
goods. By extension, amount of goods that can be purchased with a
particular monetary unit at a given time; reciprocally, price index
is the monetary amount necessary to purchase a particular good at
a given time.

PURE TONE
See Simple tone

RAD
See Absorbed dose

RADIATION
Emission,* transmission, and absorption of energy in the form of
particles such as electrons, or waves such as electromagnetic waves.

RADIATION DETECTOR
See Particle detector

RADIATION DOSIMETRY
Study of the measurement and evaluation of exposure* to ionizing
radiation,* and of its effects.

RADIATION EXPOSURE
Total quantity of ionizing radiation* measured at a given point.
Exposure dose: Amount of radiation that produces ionization of a certain amount of electrostatic charge in a volume of air of a certain mass
under given environmental conditions, such as temperature, humidity,
or pressure. Unit of measurement: roentgen. Exposure dose has been
superseded by absorbed dose* and dose equivalent.*

RADIATION INJURY
Damage to the cells of living organisms caused by ionizing radiation.*
The effect is proportional to the intensity of the radioactivity*; it
appears in a variety of forms, particularly burns, tumors, and cancer;
and it can be incremental, genetic, immediate, or delayed. Long-lived
radioactive isotopes may persist through links in the food chain,* and
concentration* may occur in ingested or inhaled substances, air and
water in particular, and in the organism.

RADIATION MONITORING
Continuous or periodic determination of the presence and amount of
ionizing radiation* in a given area, using devices such as dosimeter*
and particle detector.*

RADIATION SOURCE
Radioactive material* or device, such as accelerator or x-ray tube,
used as a controlled source of ionizing radiation* for various medical,
industrial, or other purposes.

RADIOACTIVE CONTAMINANT
See Radioactive material

RADIOACTIVE CONTAMINATION
Presence of radioactive material* of sufficient radioactivity* in places
and conditions where it may damage organisms or interfere with the
operation of certain devices, directly or by deposit in the environment.* Syn.: Radiological contamination.

RADIOACTIVE DECAY
Progressive decrease in the radioactivity* of a substance by spontaneous and continuous disintegration or transformation of a nuclide.*

RADIOACTIVE DECONTAMINATION
Removal of radioactive contaminants,* or reduction or elimination of
the radioactivity* of a medium or a substance. The decontamination
factor is the ratio of initial specific radioactivity to final specific
radioactivity, following a decontamination process. Syn.: Radiological
decontamination.

RADIOACTIVE ELEMENT
See Radioactive material

RADIOACTIVE FALLOUT
Particles of radioactive contaminant* emitted in the atmosphere* by
a nuclear explosion and descending to the earth surface by gravity or
carried by precipitation.*

RADIOACTIVE HALF-LIFE
Average time interval necessary for the radioactivity* of material
in a living organism to be reduced to half its intensity by radioactive
decay* and biological elimination.

RADIOACTIVE MATERIAL
Organic or inorganic substance containing, or composed of, one or
more constituents (radioactive elements such as radium and uranium)

that exhibit significant radioactivity.* Radioactive material can serve useful purposes or cause radioactive contamination* (<u>radioactive contaminant</u>).

RADIOACTIVE SERIES
Succession of radioactive decay* of nuclides,* resulting in progressively lighter nuclides until a stable nuclide results. The unit of measurement of this process is the <u>curie</u>, corresponding to the amount of radionuclide* that undergoes disintegration at a rate of 3.7×10^{10} per second.

RADIOACTIVE SOURCE
Radioactive material* intended for use as a source of ionizing radiation.*

RADIOACTIVITY
Emission* (and transmission) of ionizing radiation* by spontaneous disintegration of the nuclide.* By extension, the property of certain substances (radioactive material*) to emit this radiation, and the radiation itself.

RADIOBIOLOGY
Field of science, derived from biology* and radiology,* that deals with the effects of ionizing radiation* on living organisms.

RADIOECOLOGY
Field of science, derived from ecology* and radiology,* that deals with the relations among organisms, their environment,* and radioactivity.*

RADIOLOGICAL CONTAMINATION
See Radioactive contamination

RADIOLOGICAL DECONTAMINATION
See Radioactive decontamination

RADIOLOGICAL DOSE
See Absorbed dose

RADIOLOGY
Field of science, derived primarily from nuclear physics and medicine, that deals with the principles and methods of radioactivity* and the properties and application of ionizing radiation,* particularly in medicine for the diagnosis and treatment of disease.

RADIONUCLIDE
See Nuclide

RAINFALL
See Rainwater

RAINWATER
Water falling from the atmosphere* as rain and other forms of precipitation,* usually with little dissolved minerals. Called <u>rainfall</u> when referring to its amount.

RAW SEWAGE
See Liquid waste

RAW SLUDGE
See Sewage sludge

RAW WATER
See Water supply

RECESSIVE
Of, or relating to, an inherited trait* that manifests itself only when present in both genes* of the pair that determines it (<u>homozygous</u>).

RECYCLE
See Waste

REGIMEN
Flow characteristics of a stream, such as volume, velocity, or sedimentation, over time.

REGIONAL PLAN
See Urban plan

REGIONAL PLANNING
See Urban planning

RELIABILITY
Probability that a structure, apparatus, or instrument, or a part thereof, will perform its intended function satisfactorily and without failure, for a specified period and under defined conditions of use, maintenance, and environment.* Also: Degree of accuracy expected of a measurement or other data.

REM
See Dose equivalent

RENEWABLE RESOURCE
See Natural resource

REPRODUCTION RATE
See Birth rate

RESERVOIR
See Lake

RESIDUAL SUBSTANCE
Traces of chemicals used in agricultural processes, such as pesticide*
or veterinary drugs, remaining in their original or metabolized form
on or in food,* and potentially capable of causing harmful effects to
living organisms.

RESIDUE
Small, modified portion of a material or substance remaining after
an abstractive or purifying chemical or physical process, which constitutes waste* or a by-product.* Syn.: Residuum.

RESIDUUM
See Residue

RESISTANCE
Physiological or psychological process by which an organism or a
population* becomes progressively insensitized to the effects of an
environmental factor, or of a toxic or polluting substance or agent,
or fails to respond to a treatment.

RETENTION
See Accumulation

REVERBERATION
Persistence of a sound* in a fully or partially enclosed space with
minimum sound-absorption* property, due in particular to multiple
reflections, after the reception of this sound in that space has stopped.

RHIZOBIUM
See Nitrogen cycle

RILL EROSION
See Erosion

RISING STAGE
See Discharge

RIVER MOUTH
See Estuary

RODENTICIDE
See Pesticide

ROENTGEN
See Radiation exposure

ROW HOUSE
See House

RURAL SLUM
See Slum

SALINE SOIL
See Salt content

SALINITY
See Salt content

SALT CONTENT
Amount of dissolved chlorine and other halogens* present in water,
expressed as salinity or chlorinity depending on specific test conditions, measured in parts per thousand. Seawater salinity varies geo-
graphically, generally from 32 to 41 percent. Saline soil: Soil with
an excessive salt content which adversely affects its fertility,* due
in particular to poor drainage* and evaporation, and irrigation*
water, or seawater intrusion.

SALTMARSH
See Wetlands

SAMPLING
Collection of a small representative amount of data or substance of
any kind for the purpose of analysis.

SANITARY ENGINEERING
Branch of civil engineering that deals with the planning, design, construction, and operation of structures and systems, particularly for
water and wastes,* aimed at insuring the environmental health* of a
community.

SANITATION
Application of measures and techniques aimed at insuring the environmental health* of a community.

SAPROPHYTE
See Heterotroph

SAPROZOIC
See Heterotroph

SATELLITE TOWN
See Suburb

SAVOR
Combined sensation (acidity, bitterness, salinity, and sweetness) received by the taste buds (gustatory receptors) of the tongue.

SCRUBBER
Device for the removal of undesirable components from a gas stream by injection of, or passage through, a liquid. Syn.: Washer, wet collector.

SEASONAL DWELLING
See Second home

SECONDARY PRODUCTION
See Biological production

SECOND HOME
Dwelling* used during leisure time (weekend and/or vacation) in environmental conditions entirely different from those of the primary home. The increase in second-home development has brought environmental problems to rural and wilderness areas. Syn.: Seasonal dwelling.

SEDIMENTATION
Process of depositing loose material originating from the chemical weathering* of rock and transported by air or water, often accumulated in successive layers or strata,* and eventually consolidating into another rock (sedimentary rock).

SEGREGATION
See Social integration

SEMIDETACHED HOUSE
See House

SEPARATOR
Device that isolates and removes one or more components of a solid,
liquid, or gaseous mixture, using processes related to the physical,
chemical, or biological characteristics of the components, such as
particle size, solubility, or specific gravity. These processes, used
in particular for pollution* abatement, include screening, trickling,
filtration, settling, scrubbing, absorption, adsorption, coagulation,
dissolution, combustion, evaporation, condensation, precipitation,*
electrolysis, and centrifugal, magnetic, or electrostatic force.

SERVICE
Performance or result of an activity having a value to individuals and
society,* constituting an economic good,* although not a tangible
product. Includes personal assistance such as medical or legal services, performance of functions such as transportation or entertain-
ment, and provision of facilities or utilities such as housing rental
or gas distribution. Generally used in its plural form in economics.*

SEWAGE SLUDGE
Semisolid residue removed by various techniques from raw sewage*
in the treatment of liquid waste,* leaving the effluent.* Called raw
sludge prior to treatment; activated sludge after an oxidation process
involving filtration and trickling, flocculation,* aeration,* and multi-
plication of microorganisms (aerobic* decomposition); and digested
sludge after decomposition* by anaerobic* bacteria.

SHANTY TOWN
Disorderly development, sometimes quite extensive, with minimal
public services,* consisting of unsanitary shacks roughly constructed
with reclaimed materials, often built and occupied by squatters
(squatter settlement). Generally resulting in developing countries
from rural migration* to the fringe of a metropolis.*

SHEET EROSION
See Erosion

SIAL
See Lithosphere

SILT
Fine sedimentary particles, of a size between sand and clay particles
(0.002-0.05 mm). Silt from erosion,* carried and deposited by wind
and water, causes pollution* of rivers, lakes,* and reservoirs* by
suspension* and sedimentation* (siltation).

SILTATION
See Silt

SIMA
See Lithosphere

SIMPLE TONE
Sound* produced by a single sinusoidal acoustic vibration.* Syn.:
Pure tone.

SINGLE-FAMILY DWELLING
See Dwelling

SITE PLAN
See Urban plan

SLUM
Blighted area of a city,* generally with poor public services,* predominantly occupied by dilapidated, unsanitary, and/or overcrowded
dwellings* (slum dwellings), and marked by the low economic and
social conditions of its population.* Slurb: Slum located in the suburbs*
(neologism); rural slum: Slum located in a rural area; ghetto: Area,
often blighted, occupied by an ethnic minority group, originally only
Jewish.

SLUM DWELLING
See Slum

SLURB
See Slum

SMOG
Combination of smoke and fog. Acid smog results from the combination
in the atmosphere* of a smoke aerosol* retained in fog, and of gaseous
or liquid acid pollutants,* originating primarily from stationary emission* sources. Photochemical smog results from the combination of
gaseous photochemical oxidants and a liquid aerosol, originating from
solar radiation action on pollutants from motor vehicle exhausts.

SMUT
Particle of soot* carried in combustion gases and deposited on surfaces
coming in contact with it.

SOCIAL BEHAVIOR
Actions and reactions of an individual when relating to a group in a
given environment,* resulting from inherited traits* and acquired

attitudes, from environmental influences, and from group dynamics.
Group behavior: Collective social behavior of assembled individuals.

SOCIAL BENEFIT
See Social cost

SOCIAL COST
Detrimental effect or expense imputable to an economic activity, and
not borne by the economic unit* immediately involved, but by other
economic units not directly involved in this activity, or by government or society* as a whole. Social costs can be diffuse or concentrated, immediate or deferred, perceptible or not, monetary or
nonmonetary. Antonym: Social benefit.

SOCIAL GOOD
See Good

SOCIAL INDICATOR
See Environmental indicator

SOCIAL INTEGRATION
Insertion into an established society* or community of a social group
and its individual members, whose characteristics and origins differ
markedly from those of that society or community. Characterized by
adaptation* to, commingling with, and acceptance by this society,
equitable sharing of its resources, and participation in its social
structure. Desegregation: Elimination of segregation. Antonym:
Segregation.

SOCIAL MOBILITY
Ability and tendency of individuals or groups to change their social
position, as defined by income, occupation, political or civic participation, and other aspects. The change itself. Vertical—and upward—
mobility refers to the value ranking of these positions.

SOCIETY
Population* group sharing common culture, institutions, and economic
resources.

SOIL
Loose material covering the earth's bedrock, capable of supporting
plant growth, resulting from the weathering of the bedrock and the
decomposition* of organic matter, under physical, chemical, and
biological action of the environment.* Soils are classified according
to their physical, chemical, or agricultural capability characteristics.

SOIL CONSERVATION
Management practices used to stop the erosion* and deterioration
of a soil* and restore its fertility.*

SOIL DEPLETION
See Soil deterioration

SOIL DETERIORATION
Modification of the physical and chemical properties of a soil,* which
reduces its fertility.* Caused by natural or man-made processes,
such as erosion,* depletion (reduction in nutrient* content), leaching,*
or salt buildup.

SOIL FERTILITY
Capacity of the soil* to produce plant crops. Depends on climatic and
soil conditions, particularly organic matter content, and types of
plant cultivated.

SOIL GENESIS
Processes of formation of soil* from the parent material, particularly
by chemical weathering,* and evolution of its characteristics under
the influence of environmental factors over a period of time. Can be
altered by improvement of the soil (by fertilization or irrigation), or
by its depletion (as by erosion* or podzolization*). Syn.: Pedogenesis.

SOIL HORIZON
Layer of soil* with distinguishing characteristics, generally parallel
to the surface, pertaining to a distinct phase of its evolution. Syn.:
Stratum.

SOIL IMPROVEMENT
Operation modifying the physical and chemical properties of a soil*
in order to improve its fertility.*

SOIL MECHANICS
Principles and techniques of solid and fluid mechanics and of engineering geology, pertaining to the physical properties of soils,*
applied to the design, construction, and maintenance of structures
and earthwork.

SOIL PROFILE
Vertical cross-section through a soil,* showing the various horizons
from the surface down to the parent material.

SOIL SCIENCE
Field of science that deals with soils,* their formation, properties, classification, use, mapping, and other aspects. Syn.: Pedology.

SOMATIC
Of, or relating to, cells other than germ cells. By extension, noninherited or nonhereditary. Antonym: Germinal: Of, or relating to, the germ cells. By extension, inherited or hereditary (genetics). Relating to the body, as distinguished from the mind or the environment* (health).

SONIC BOOM
Noise* caused by a shock wave emanating from an aircraft or missile traveling at or above the local speed of sound.*

SOOT
Aerosol* rich in carbon and oil compounds resulting from the incomplete combustion of coal, oil, wood, or other fuels.

SOUND
Sensation perceived by the sense of hearing (auditory sensation) caused by an acoustic vibration.* Sounds have broad-range physiological, psychological, and social effects.

SOUND ABSORPTION
Reduction of the sound energy* of a sound* traveling through a medium or striking the surface separating two media. Property of a material or medium to absorb sound energy.

SOUND-ABSORPTION COEFFICIENT
Fraction of the incident sound energy* absorbed by a material or an object, under specified conditions, such as angle of incidence, frequency, and sound-field diffusion.

SOUND ATTENUATION
Reduction of the sound intensity* of a sound propagating in a medium, measured by the difference in sound level* recorded between two points along the line of propagation within this medium or at its boundaries. Property of a material or medium to reduce the intensity of a sound transmitted through it.

SOUND ENERGY
Difference between the total energy in a given part of a medium, and the energy that would exist with no sound* waves present.

SOUND-ENERGY FLUX DENSITY
See Sound intensity

SOUND INTENSITY
Average rate of sound energy* transmitted through a unit area normal
to the specified direction, expressed in watts per square meter. The
auditory mechanism is primarily sensitive to sound intensity. Syn.:
Sound-energy flux density, sound-power density.

SOUND-INTENSITY LEVEL
Value in decibels* of ten times the logarithm to the base ten of the
ratio of the sound intensity* radiated by a given source to a reference
intensity (commonly one picowatt per square meter).

SOUND LEVEL
Sound-pressure level* averaged over the audio frequency* range and
modified by weighting factors for different frequency characteristics.
Weightings, referred to as A, B, and C, adjust physical field measurements to approximate values of physiological auditory sensation.
Equivalent sound level: Level of a constant sound equivalent to the
sound level of a time-varying sound averaged over a specified time
interval. Abbreviated: $L_{eq(x)}$, x being the time interval.

SOUND-LEVEL METER
Instrument for the measurement of sound levels,* normally calibrated
in decibels* and including electrical weighting networks.

SOUND POWER
Sound energy* emitted by a given source per unit of time, measured
in ergs per second or watts. Syn.: Acoustic power.

SOUND-POWER DENSITY
See Sound intensity

SOUND-POWER LEVEL
Value in decibels* of ten times the logarithm to the base ten of the
ratio of the sound power* radiated by a given source to a reference
power (commonly one picowatt). Used to define a source noise independently from the acoustic characteristics of its environment.*

SOUND PRESSURE
Difference between the instantaneous pressure at a point in a medium
in the presence of a sound wave, and the static pressure* at that point.

SOUND-PRESSURE LEVEL
Value in decibels* of 20 times the logarithm to the base ten of the
ratio of the pressure of a given sound* to a reference pressure (commonly 20 micropascals or 0.0002 microbar). Used to define noise*
in a given environment,* and to define the source noise, taking account
of its distance. Abbreviated: SPL.

SOUND SPECTRUM
Description of the sound level* of the components of a sound* in
function of frequency, graphically expressed in a spectrogram.

SOURCE OF EMISSION
See Emission

SOURCE OF POLLUTION
See Emission

SPECIFIC ABSORBED DOSE
See Absorbed dose

SPECTROGRAM
See Sound spectrum

SPILLOVER
See Externality

SPOIL BANK
See Spoil heap

SPOIL HEAP
Residual solid waste* material, particularly overburden, from
excavation and mining operations, piled up on adjoining land. Often
defaces the landscape and causes soil* and water pollution* through
runoff and leaching.* These effects can be limited by land-
reclamation* measures, including land shaping, soil building, and
planting. Syn.: Spoil bank.

SPRING
Emergence of groundwater* at one point of the ground surface (WHO).
Springwater may emerge polluted by infiltration, intrusion, or ground-
metals or minerals.

SQUATTER SETTLEMENT
See Shanty town

STACK SOLIDS
Particulate* carried in combustion gases.

STANDARD
See Criterion

STANDARD OF CONSUMPTION
See Standard of living

STANDARD OF LIVING
Material conditions of necessities, comforts,* and luxuries, considered essential for the survival of the individuals of a group, and desirable for their biological, psychological, and social well-being.* By
extension, the actual level of material well-being achieved by a
particular group, based on its real purchasing power* (level of living).
Economic measurement of standard of living is expressed in monetary
terms as the value of goods* and services* consumed (standard of
consumption), or alternatively, as the price to consumers of acquiring
them (cost of living). Components such as working or health conditions,
leisure-time availability, or environmental quality are generally not
adequately reflected in these measurements. Life style: Particular
choice made from among the variety of available goods and services
by individuals and groups in exercising their purchasing power.*

STATIC PRESSURE
Pressure that would exist at a point in a medium, in the absence of
sound waves. Equivalent to atmospheric pressure when the medium
is the atmosphere.*

STATIONARY SOURCE
See Emission

STRATUM
See Soil horizon

STREAMFLOW
See Discharge

STREET FURNITURE
See Urban design

SUBSONIC
See Infrasonic vibration

SUBSURFACE DRAINAGE
See Drainage

SUBSURFACE WATER
See Groundwater

SUBURB
Urbanized fringe area of a city,* mostly residential (dormitory suburb), initially depending on the central city for much of its needs, and sometimes becoming an autonomous, incorporated community* (satellite town). Collectively: Suburbia. Exurb: Generally upper-income, scattered residential development beyond the urban fringe (neologism). Collectively: Exurbia.

SUPERSONIC
See Ultrasonic vibration

SURFACE-ACTIVE AGENT
See Surfactant

SURFACE DRAINAGE
See Drainage

SURFACE MINING
Extraction of mineral and metal ore by various methods from surface deposits or shallow seams. Dredge tailings* from placer mining, waste* dumps from open-pit mining, and overburden from strip mining, cause water pollution* and land disfiguration, requiring extensive land reclamation* to restore its usability and environmental quality.

SURFACE RUNOFF
Water from precipitation* in excess of evaporation, infiltration, interception, or storage capacity, and flowing overland to waterways of the drainage basin.* Initial surface runoff of a storm often contains debris, oil, fertilizers,* and other pollutants.*

SURFACE WATER
Water flowing or stagnant on the earth surface (oceans, lakes,* streams, and glaciers). In oceanography,* top layer of the ocean water subjected to wave action, also called mixed layer.

SURFACTANT
Soluble active agent of various kinds (anionic, cationic, nonionic, ampholytic) used in detergents* to loosen and dissolve dirt by reducing the surface tension of the liquid. Causes foam and resists sewage treatment. Syn.: Surface-active agent.

SUSPENDED SOLID
See Turbidity

SUSPENSION
Condition in which fine solid particles are distributed in a medium.
These particles are usually referred to as particulate matter* in
gases, and suspended solids* in liquids. Measured in grams per liter
or parts per million. Emulsion: Condition in which a liquid is dispersed in another without mixing to a point of achieving a colloidal
state or solution. Dispersion: Movement of particles in a medium
resulting in a nonuniform distribution; diffusion: movement resulting
in a uniform distribution. Precipitation: Natural or induced process
of separation of the suspended solids from a liquid or gaseous medium.

SWAMP
See Wetlands

SYMBIOSIS
See Ecological interaction

SYNECOLOGY
See Ecology

SYNERGISM
Action of two or more substances, agents, or organisms in association,
whose total effect is greater than the sum of the individual effects,
reinforces the effect of one or more of the individual components, or
brings benefits to each of the individuals. Syn.: Mutualism.

TAILINGS
Residual waste* material from processing operations such as mining,
milling, or distilling, deposited in loose or fluid form on the land.

TERATOGEN
Substance or agent inducing a congenital* anomaly* (birth defect) in
an embryo.

TERRITORIALITY
See Territory

TERRITORY
Living space of varying range appropriated by an animal, a pair, or
a population of animals, for dwelling, mating, ensuring a food* supply,
and raising progeny. In some cases clearly defined and protected
against intruders. Territoriality: Pattern of behavior by which an
animal appropriates a territory.

THERMAL EFFLUENT
See Thermal pollution

THERMAL ENVIRONMENT
Normal temperature range and thermal cyclical changes specific to
a biotope,* and suitable to sustain its biocenose.*

THERMAL POLLUTION
Raising of the temperature of a body of water by the discharge* of
heated effluents (thermal effluent) from industrial installations, cooling
systems, or geothermal subsurface water.* Thermal pollution is
reduced by passing the effluents through cooling towers and reservoirs*
before discharge into waterways. Water temperature rises can signif-
icantly affect the aquatic biota,* the potability of the water, and its
taste and odor, through increased volatility of components and stimulated growth of organisms. Syn.: Thermopollution.

THERMONUCLEAR FUSION
See Nuclear fusion

THERMOPOLLUTION
See Thermal pollution

THRESHOLD
Distinct point on a scale of increasing or decreasing values in a process
or a changing condition, beyond which certain phenomena or effects
occur, or certain conditions are met. This point is called critical,
such as in critical state, critical temperature, or critical speed.

THRESHOLD OF AUDIBILITY
Minimum effective sound-pressure level* of a specified constant sound,
for a determined frequency, causing an auditory sensation in a given
listener, measured in decibels.* Sensation levels above the threshold
of audibility are called thresholds of feeling, discomfort,* and pain.
Syn.: Threshold of detectability.

THRESHOLD OF DETECTABILITY
See Threshold of audibility

THRESHOLD OF DISCOMFORT
See Threshold of audibility

THRESHOLD OF FEELING
See Threshold of audibility

THRESHOLD OF PAIN
See Threshold of audibility

TIDAL WETLANDS
See Wetlands

TIDELAND
Coastal land under water at high tide and uncovered at low tide,
possessing unique ecological characteristics. Called tidal wetland*
when normally water saturated. Syn.: Intertidal zone.

TOLERANCE
Relative ability of an organism to endure without physiological or
psychological modification (trauma), the effects of an unfavorable
environmental factor, or of a toxic or polluting substance or agent.
Tolerance limit: Maximum level, intensity, accumulation,* or duration of a factor, substance, or agent that can be endured by an
organism before physiological or psychological modifications occur.

TOLERANCE LIMIT
See Tolerance

TOXICOLOGY
Study of poisonous substances, their nature, detection, effects, and
methods of treatment.

TOXIN
Substance secreted by certain living organisms, capable of causing
harmful effects to—and of stimulating production of a neutralizing
antitoxin by—a receiving organism. Toxins can be produced by
fungi* (mycotoxins), plants (phytotoxins), animals (zootoxins), or
bacteria (bacterial toxins). Bacterial toxins are either excreted
normally (exotoxins), or retained inside the bacteria and released
only after their disintegration (endotoxins).

TOWN
See City

TOWN HOUSE
See House

TRACE ELEMENT
See Micronutrient

TRAUMA
See Tolerance

TREATED SEWAGE
See Liquid waste

TROPHIC ACCUMULATION
See Accumulation

TROPHIC LEVEL
See Food chain

TURBIDITY
Cloudy appearance of water and other liquids due to colloidal droplets
or fine particles in suspension* (suspended solids). Has a variety of
effects on the ecosystem.* Measured by the loss of light intensity,
using a turbidimeter, Secchi disc, or other means. Can be reduced
and eliminated by flocculation, a process in which suspended solids
are assembled into floccules, or flocs, by addition of coagulant chemicals (flocculants or clarifying agents), stirring of the liquid, followed
by settlement and decantation.

TWO-FAMILY DWELLING
See Dwelling

ULTRASONIC VIBRATION
Vibration whose frequency is above the audio frequency* range (over
20,000 cycles per second, or hertzes) and therefore not audible by
man. Ultrasonic vibrations can nevertheless produce disturbing
effects, felt only near the source, as they decrease rapidly in their
propagation through the air. "Ultrasonic" is not to be confused with
supersonic which refers to speeds higher than the speed of sound.*

URBAN COMMUNITY
Group of individuals and families living in an identifiable human
settlement* or part thereof, constituting a social entity bound together
in varying degrees by common interests and values, community facilities,* local government,* and economic interdependence.

URBAN DESIGN
Art and techniques aimed at giving esthetic and functional form to the
urban environment, through the planning of sites, the architecture of
buildings, the landscaping of open spaces, and the design of traffic
arteries and street furniture (signs, lights, fountains, planting boxes,
benches, waste baskets, and other fixtures). Also the result of this
activity. Syn.: Community design.

URBAN INFRASTRUCTURE
Public and private community facilities* and utilities, such as storm
drains or telephone systems, necessary for the performance of urban
services.*

URBANIZATION
Transformation of land from rural to urban use, resulting from eco-
nomic, demographic, and spatial growth of an urban center. Also:
Increasing concentration of a population* in urban places.

URBANIZED AREA
Territory encompassing a city,* its suburbs,* and urban extensions,
such as airports, parks, and stadiums. Urbanizing area also includes
undeveloped land in the path of approaching urbanization.*

URBANIZING AREA
See Urbanized area

URBAN PLAN
Set of documents and maps resulting from the urban planning* process,
adopted as community development policies by a local government,*
and implemented by regulatory measures, and capital investment and
management programs. The plan is comprehensive (covering the entire
territory of the community, and all the urban functions), generalized
(not site-specific), flexible (subject to interpretation), long-range
(commonly twenty years), and evolutionary (requiring periodic updating
in response to changes in conditions and objectives). Syn.: Development plan, general plan, comprehensive plan, master plan, community plan. Plans at other scales and for different purposes are: site
plans at the project level, and regional plans at the county, metropolitan, state, or interstate level.

URBAN PLANNING
Arts, sciences, and techniques that together contribute to the organization, development, and evolution of urban areas and their urbanizing
environs, based on economic, social, legal, and esthetic concepts and
conditions, in order to promote the welfare of the public and the quality
of the environment,* within the administrative and political process
of government. Regional planning is the application of similar principles and techniques to an entire region.

URBAN REDEVELOPMENT
Planned local government* program, usually with federal assistance,
involving acquisition and clearance of slums,* relocation of their
inhabitants, assembly of land, construction of urban infrastructure,* and

sale of land to private builders and public agencies for a variety of uses. Redevelopment projects often have adverse effects on the existing social structure of a neighborhood* or urban community.*

URBAN RENEWAL
Planned, concerted public and private actions to improve the environment* of existing urban areas, prevent further decay, and adjust to new economic and social needs and objectives. Renewal measures include housing rehabilitation,* historic restoration, code enforcement, redevelopment,* redesign of traffic systems, provision of new—and upgrading of old—community facilities* and urban infrastructure.* Neighborhood conservation is the application of renewal measures at the neighborhood* level.

URBAN SOCIOLOGY
Field of social science that deals with human social behavior in an urban environment.* Other related fields include human ecology, urban pathology, and environmental psychology.

VECTOR
Intermediate carrier agent, such as an insect, transmitting pathogens* from one host* to another.

VILLAGE
See City

VIRUCIDE
See Pesticide

WANT
Need or desire expressed by individuals or society* for certain goods,* not necessarily accompanied by the ability to obtain them. Generally used in its plural form in economics.*

WASHER
See Scrubber

WASTE
Solid, liquid, or gaseous material or substance remaining from human activities, particularly from the production, processing, and consumption* of goods.* Due to the large and continuous production and frequent toxicity of wastes, their disposal into the environment* is the major cause of pollution.* The most effective, but generally costly, method of elimination of wastes is to recover and recycle them, by various treatments and processes, as reusable by-products.

WASTE WATER
See Liquid waste

WATER CATCHMENT
See Water diversion

WATER CYCLE
See Hydrologic cycle

WATER DIVERSION
Removal, generally by gravity, of a portion of stream water from its natural course by dike, dam,* tunnel, gate, canal, and other works, for various purposes such as domestic supply, irrigation,* power production, or flood control. Syn.: Water catchment (Brit.).

WATER DIVIDE
See Drainage basin

WATER EROSION
See Erosion

WATER HARDNESS
Amount of metal ions, commonly calcium and magnesium carbonates, dissolved in water, measured in parts per million or mg/1. Excessive hardness, generally regarded as over 150 ppm, is considered objectionable in domestic* and industrial* water. Water softening by various water treatment* processes reduces the content of calcium and magnesium salts.

WATER-HOLDING CAPACITY
Maximum amount of water which a specific soil* can retain by molecular attraction (that is, excluding gravitational water), measured by weight as a proportion of water to soil, under laboratory conditions. Field capacity is water-holding capacity measured in depth of rainfall* in the field.

WATER PURIFICATION
See Water treatment

WATER QUALITY
Biological, chemical, and physical characteristics of water necessary to insure its healthy, harmless, and pleasant use. Water is generally treated at the water supply* intake (water treatment*), and after use (liquid waste* treatment), to control toxic or infectious agents, objectionable taste or order, turbidity,* coloration, hardness, alkalinity, salinity,* dissolved oxygen, foaming agents, or temperature.

WATER RESOURCE MANAGEMENT
Study, planning, monitoring,* and application of quantitative and
qualitative control and development techniques for long-term, multiple
use of the diverse forms of water resources. Intensive use of water
resources for increased human consumption* through development of
water projects generally brings about major modifications in the
biota.*

WATERSHED
See Drainage basin

WATER SOFTENING
See Water hardness

WATER SUPPLY
Raw water collected, stored, transported, distributed, and when
necessary purified, for various consumptive purposes such as for the
community (domestic water and drinking water), industry (industrial
water), or agriculture (irrigation water), all having different quality
requirements.

WATER TABLE
See Groundwater

WATER TREATMENT
Processing of raw water* to increase its biological, chemical, and/or
physical qualities. Processes vary, depending on the characteristics
of the raw water and its intended usage. They include chlorination,
ozonization, demineralization, desalination, fluoridation, or softening.
Syn.: Water purification.

WELL-BEING
State of physical and psychological health* and adjustment to a given
environment,* as perceived by an individual.

WET COLLECTOR
See Scrubber

WETLANDS
Waterlogged or shallow-water land possessing unique ecological characteristics, which constitutes the essential habitat* of certain flora
and fauna, such as waterfowl. The reclamation of wetlands, by
draining, diking, and filling, for agriculture and eradication of
malaria-bearing mosquitoes in particular, has endangered or

destroyed many species. Called <u>marsh</u> when covered predominantly
with grass and reeds, <u>swamp</u> when covered predominantly with shrubs
and trees, and <u>tidal wetlands</u> and <u>saltmarsh</u> when located in the
coastal zone* and containing saline or brackish water.

WILDERNESS AREA
Tract of land retaining a substantially primeval character of land
forms, flora, and fauna, and of sufficient size to maintain an ecosystem* largely free from human influence, generally protected from
development by government action, for recreational, educational, and
scientific use. Syn.: <u>Primitive area</u>.

WILDLIFE REFUGE
Area particularly suited for the protection and enhancement of specific
wild animal populations,* set aside, generally by government action,
for recreational, educational, and scientific use.

WILD RIVER
Stream, its shores and valley, or segment thereof, with special
natural values, retained in primitive and free-flowing conditions, for
recreational, educational, and scientific use, generally through governmental action. Land forms, flora, and fauna are protected, and
development is precluded for such purposes as water diversion* or
effluent* discharge,* dams,* dikes or channelization, roads or
bridges, mining, agriculture or timber production.

WIND EROSION
See Erosion

YIELD
Agricultural productivity* estimated in relation to the area unit under
cultivation (yield per acre). Measures leading to excessive increase
in yield can result in deterioration* of the soil.*

ZONE
See Zoning

ZONE OF AERATION
See Aquifer

ZONE OF SATURATION
See Aquifer

ZONING

Division of the territory of a local government's* jurisdiction, by ordinance, into districts or zones, shown on a zoning map, within which apply uniform regulations controlling the use and coverage of the land, and the location, density, use and height of structures. Major tool for the short term, precise implementation of the urban plan* and of specific objectives of environmental quality, public safety, economic values, and orderly growth of the community.

ZONING MAP
See Zoning

ZOOGEOGRAPHY
See Biogeography

ZOOPLANKTON
See Plankton

ZOOTOXIN
See Toxin

English	French	German
abiotic	abiotique	abiotisch
absorbed dose	dose absorbée	absorbierte Dosis
acclimatation	acclimatation	Akklimatisation
acclimatizazation	acclimatation	Akklimatisation
accumulation	accumulation	Akkumulation
acid smog	smog acide	saurer Smog
acoustic disturbance	bruit perturbateur	Störgeräusch
acoustic power	puissance acoustique	Schalleistung
acoustics	acoustique	Akustik
acoustic signal	signal acoustique	—
acoustic vibration	vibration acoustique	Schallschwingung
activated carbon	charbon actif	Aktivkohle
activated charcoal	charbon actif	Aktivkohle
activated sludge	boues activées	Belebtschlamm
adaptation	adaptation	Adaptation
adjuvant	adjuvant	Zusatz
adjuvant treatment	traitement adjuvant	Zusatzbehandlung
adulterant	adultérant	Fälschungsmittel
aeration	aération	Lüftung
aerator	aérateur	Belüfter
aerobic	aérobie	aerob
aerobic decomposition	décomposition aérobie	Aerobenzerfall
aerosol	aérosol	Aerosol
aerosol propellant	propulseur d'aérosol	aerosol Treibstoff
age	age	Alter
age interval	tranche d'age	Altersklasse
age-specific birth rate	taux des naissances par tranche d'age	Geburtsrate nach Altersgruppe
age-specific death rate	taux de mortalité par tranche d'age	Sterberate nach Altersgruppe
aging process	processus de vieillissement	Alterungsverfahren
aggregate	agrégat	Aggregat
alga	algue	Alge
algae bloom	floraison d'algue	Algenblüte
algicide	algicide	Algizid
allergen	allergène	Allergen
allergy	allergie	Allergie
allogenic	allogène	allogen

alluvial deposit	dépot alluvial	Alluvialablagerung
alluvion	alluvion	Alluvium
alluvium	alluvion	Alluvium
ambiance	ambiance	Umweltfaktoren
ambient noise	bruit d'ambiance	Umgebungzgeräusch
ammonification	ammonification	Ammonifikation
anaerobic	anaérobie	anaerob
anaphylaxis	anaphylaxie	Anaphylaxie
animal association	groupement animal	Tiergruppierung
animal community	communauté animale	Tiergesellschaft
anomaly	anomalie	Unregelmässigkeit
anomie	anomie	Anomie
antitoxin	antitoxine	Antitoxin
apartment house	immeuble d'habitation	Wohngebäude
aquaculture	aquaculture	Aquakultur
aquiculture	aquiculture	Aquakultur
aquifer	aquifère	Aquifer
artificial radio- activity	radioactivité artificielle	künstliche Radio- aktivität
assimilation	assimilation	Assimilation
atmosphere	atmosphère	Atmosphäre
atmospheric sciences	sciences atmosphériques	atmosphärische Wissenschaft
atomic pile	pile atomique	Atomreaktor
atomic reactor	réacteur atomique	Atomreaktor
audio frequency	fréquence audible	Tonfrequenz
audiogram	audiogramme	Audiogramm
audiometer	audiomètre	Audiometer
audio range	domaine des fréquences audibles	Frequenzumfang des Gehörs
auditory environment	environnement sonore	Klangumgebung
auditory sensation area	aire d'audition	Klangempfindungs- gebiet
autecology	autoécologie	Autoökologie
autochthonous	autochtone	eingeboren
autotroph	organisme autotrophe	autotrophischer Organismus
background noise	bruit de fond	Grundgeräusch
background radiation	rayonnement de fond	Grundstrahlung
bacterial toxin	toxine bacterienne	Bakterientoxin
bactericide	bactéricide	Bakterizid
benthic	benthique	benthonisch
benthos	benthos	Benthos
biocenose	biocénose	Biozönose

biochemical oxygen demand	demande biochimique en oxygène—DBO	biochemischer Sauerstoffbedarf—BSB
biocide	biocide	Biozid
biodegradable	biodégradable	biodegradabel
biodynamic	biodynamique	biodynamik
biogeochemical cycle	cycle biogéo-chimique	biogeochemischer Zyklus
biogeography	biogéographie	Biogeographie
biological age	age biologique	biologisches Alter
biological balance	équilibre biologique	biologische Gleich-gewicht
biological control	lutte biologique	biologische Schädlings-bekampfung
biological cycle	cycle biologique	biologischer Zyklus
biological half-life	période biologique	biologische Halb-wertzeit
biological indicator	indicateur écologique	ökologischer Indikator
biological production	production biologique	biologische Produktion
biological produc-tivity	productivité biologique	biologische Produk-tivität
biology	biologie	Biologie
biomass	biomasse	Biomasse
biomass pyramid	pyramide des biomasses	Biomassenpyramide
biome	biome	Biom
biosphere	biosphère	Biosphäre
biota	biote	Biota
biotic	biotique	biotisch
biotope	biotope	Biotop
birth rate	taux de natalité	Geburtenziffer
black tide	marée noire	Ölpest
BOD test	test de DBO	BSB-Test
buffer strip	coupure verte	Grünsektor
buffer zone	zone tampon	Pufferzone
by-product	sous-produit	Nebenprodukt
capital good	bien d'investissement	Investitionsgut
carbon cycle	cycle du carbone	Kohlenstaffzyklus
carcinogen	cancérogène	Kanzerogen
carrying capacity	capacité de charge	Aufnahmefähigkeit
case fatality rate	taux de létalité	Letalziffer
catchment area	bassin versant	—
chemical control	lutte chimique	chemische Schädlings-bekampfung

chemical oxygen demand	demande chimique en oxygène—DCO	chemischer Sauerstoff-bedarf—CSB
chemical weathering	effritement chimique	chemische Verwitterung
chemosynthesis	chimiosynthèse	chemosynthese
chlorinity	chlorinité, teneur en chlorure	Chlorgehalt
chromosome	chromosome	Chromosom
chronological age	age chronologique	kalendarisches Alter
city	ville	Stadt
climate	climat	Klima
climatic region	région climatique	klimatischer Bereich
climatic zone	zone climatique	Klimazone
climax	climax	Klimax
coastal zone	zone côtière	Küstenzone
COD test	test de DCO	CSB-Test
colloid	colloïde	Kolloid
colluvium	colluvion	Colluvium
comfort	confort	Komfort
comfort zone	zone de confort	Komfortzone
commensalism	commensalisme	Kommensalismus
commodity	—	—
community design	esthétique urbaine	städtebauliche Gestaltung
community facility	équipement collectif	Gemeinschaftsein-richtungen
community noise equivalent level	—	Gemeindegeräusch-äquivalenz
community noise rating	—	—
community partici-pation	participation	Beteiligung
community plan	schéma directeur d'aménagement et d'urbanisme	Flächennutzungsplan
complex tone	son complexe	Tongemisch
compost	compost	Kompost
comprehensive plan	schéma directeur d'aménagement et d'urbanisme	Flächennutzungsplan
concentration	concentration	Konzentration
congenital	congénital	kongenital
consumer	consommateur	Konsument, Verbraucher
consumer good	bien de consommation	Verbrauchergut
consumer society	société de consommation	Verbraucher-gesellschaft
consumption	consommation	Verbrauch

contagion	contagion	Ansteckung
contaminant	contaminant	Kontaminierungs- mittel
contamination	contamination	Kontamination
conurbation	conurbation	Zusammenwachsen
corrosion	corrosion	Korrosion
cosmic radiation	rayonnement cosmique	kosmische Strahlung
cosmic rays	rayons cosmiques	kosmische Strahlung
cost-benefit analysis	analyse coût- avantage	Kosten-Nutzen-Analyse
cost-effectiveness analysis	analyse coût- efficacité	Kostenwirksamkeits- analyse
cost of living	coût de la vie	Kosten der Lebens- haltung
critical	critique	kritisch
criterion	critère	Kriterien
crop rotation	rotation des cultures	Fruchtwechsel
crude birth rate	taux brut des naissances	Bruttogeburtsrate
crude death rate	taux brut de mortalité	Bruttosterberate
cultural practices	procédés culturaux	Kultivierungsprozesse
cumulative effect	effet cumulatif	Kumulationeffekt
curie	curie	Curie
dam	barrage	Staudamm
death rate	taux de mortalité	Sterbenziffer
death rate by cause of death	taux de mortalité par cause	Sterbenziffer nach Todesursache geordnet
decibel	décibel	Dezibel
decomposer	minéralisateur	Mineralisator
decomposition	décomposition	Zerlegung
decontamination factor	facteur de décontamination	Dekontaminierungs- faktor
defoliant	défoliant	Entlaubungsmittel
degree of adaptability	degré d'adaptabilité	Adaptationfänigkeit
demand schedule	—	Bedarfplan
demography	démographie	Demographie
denaturation	dénaturation	Entartung
denitrification	dénitrification	Denitrifikation
desegregation	déségrégation	Trennung
desiccant	défanant	Entlaubungsmittel
detached house	maison isolée	Einzelhaus
detergent	lessive, détergent	Lauge, Reinigungsmittel

development plan	schéma directeur d'aménagement et d'urbanisme	Flächennutzungsplan
dietary deficiency	carence alimentaire	Mangel
dietetics	diététique	Diätetik
diffusion	diffusion	Diffusion
digested sludge	boues digérées	zersetzter Schlamm
discharge	décharge, débit d'un fluide	Durchsatz
discomfort	gêne	Behinderung
disinfectant	désinfectant	Disinfektionsmittel
dispersion	dispersion	Dispersion
dispersion medium	milieu de dispersion	Dispersionsmittel
dispersion model	modèle de dispersion	Dispersionsmodel
DNA molecule	molécule ADN	DNA-Molekül
domestic waste	eaux usées domestiques	Haushaltsabwässer
domestic water	eaux domestiques	Haushaltwässer
dominance	dominance	Dominanz
dormitory suburb	banlieue dortoir	Schlafaussenbezirk
dose equivalent	équivalent de dose	Dosisäquivalent
dose equivalent rate	débit d'équivalent de dose	Dosisäquivalent- leistung
dosimeter	dosimètre	Dosismesser
drainage	drainage, assèchement	Entwässerung, Dränage
drainage basin	bassin hydrographique	Einzugsgebiet
drinking water	eau potable	Trinkwasser
droplet	vésicule	Bläschen
drying agent	—	—
duplex	duplex	Doppelhaus
dust separator	dépoussiéreur	Entstaubungsaggregat
dwelling	habitation	Wohnung
dwelling unit	cellule d'habitation	Wohnzelle
ecological community	communauté biotique	biotische Gesellschaft
ecological interaction	interaction biotique	biotische Wechelbezie- hungen
ecological niche	niche écologique	ökologische Nische
ecological pyramid	pyramide écologique	ökologische Pyramide
ecology	écologie	Ökologie
econometrics	économétrie	Oekonometrie
economic development	développement économique	wirtschaftliche Ent- wicklung

economic expansion	expansion économique	wirtschaftliche Expansion
economic good	bien marchand	Wirtschaftsgut
economic growth	croissance économique	Wirtschaftswachstum
economics	économie	Wirtschaftswissenschaft
economic unit	agent économique	Wirtschaftseinheit
ecosystem	écosystème	Ökosystem
ecotone	zone de transition	Übergangzone
ecotype	écotype	Ökotyp
ectoparasite	ectoparasite	Ektoparasit
edaphic	édaphique	edaphisch
edaphon	édaphon	Edaphon
effective demand	demande effective	tatsächliche Nachfrage
effective half-life	période effective	effektive Halbwertzeit
effectiveness	efficacité	Wirkungsgrad
efficiency	efficacité	Wirksamkeit
effluent	eaux usées traitées	Abwasser
emigration	émigration	Auswanderung
emission	émission	Immission
emulsion	émulsion	Emulsion
endangered species	espèce menacée d'extinction	gefährdete Art
endemism	endémie	Endemie
endogenous	endogène	endogen
endoparasite	endoparasite	Endoparasit
endotoxin	endotoxine	Endotoxin
energy pyramid	pyramide energétique	Energiepyramide
environment	environnement	Umwelt
environmental health	hygiène du milieu	Umwelthygiene
environmental indicator	indicateur de l'environnement	Umweltindikator
environmental noise	bruit du milieu	Umweltlärm
enzyme	enzyme	Enzym
epidemic	épidémie	Epidemie
epidemiology	épidémiologie	Epidemiologie
equivalent sound level	niveau acoustique équivalent	äquivalenter Schallpegel
erosion	érosion	Erosion
estuary	estuaire	weite Flussmündung
ethology	éthologie	Ethologie
eutrophic	eutrophique	eutrophisch
eutrophication	eutrophisation	Eutrophierung
exogenous	exogène	exogen
exotoxin	exotoxine	Exotoxin

exposure	exposition	Aussetzung
exposure dose	dose d'exposition	Strahlendosis
expressivity	expressivité	Expressivität
external diseconomy	déséconomie externe	externe Wirt-schaftsstörung
external economy	économie externe	externe Wirtschaft
externality	externalité	Externität
exurb	grande banlieue	Aussenbezirke
factor of production	facteur de production	Produktionsfaktor
falling stage	décrue	zurückgehendes Hochwasser
fallow land	terre en jachère	Brachfeld
family planning	planification familiale des naissances	Familienplanung
fast breeder reactor	surrégénerateur	Brutreaktor
fatigue	fatigue	Ermüdung
fecundity	fécondité	Fruchtbarkeit
feedstuff	pâture	Futtermittel
ferment	ferment	Ferment
fermentation	fermentation	Fermentation
fertile material	matière fertile	Brutstoff
fertility	fécondité	Fruchtbarkeitsziffer
fertilizer	engrais	Düngemittel
field capacity	capacité au champ	Feldkapazität
fissile material	matière fissile	thermische spaltbares Material
fissionable material	matière fissile	Spaltmaterial
flavor	flaveur	Geruch
flocculant	coagulant	Flockig
flocculation	floculation	Flockung
floccule	flocon	Flocke
flocs	flocs	Flocke
flood stage	inondation	Hochwasser
fly ash	cendre volante	Flugasche
food	aliment	Nahrungsmittel
food additive	additif alimentaire	Lebensmittelzusatz
food chain	chaîne alimentaire	Nahrungskette
food irradiation	radioconservation	Strahlenkonservierung
food product	produit alimentaire	Nahrungsmittelprodukte
foodstuff	denrée alimentaire	Lebensmittel
food web	réseau trophique	Nahrungsnetz
forest management	gestion des forêts	Waldbewirtschaftung
forestry	sylviculture	Forstwirtschaft
free good	bien hors marché	Freigut
freeze drying	lyophilisation	Gefriertrochnung

fungicide	fongicide	Fungizid
fungus	champignon	Pilz
futurology	prospective	Prospektive
gene	gène	Gen
gene pool	fond commun de gènes, capital génétique d'une espèce	gemeinsame Genbasis, genetische Substanz
general plan	schéma directeur d'aménagement et d'urbanisme	Flächennutzungsplan
genetic damage	dommage génétique	Genschäden
genetic inheritance	patrimoine héréditaire	Erbgut
genetic load	fardeau génétique	genetische Belastung
genetic map	carte génétique	genetische Karte
genetic polymorphism	polymorphisme génétique	genetischer Polymorphismus
genetics	génétique	genetik Vererbungslehre
genetic variation	variation génétique	genetische Variation
genotype	génotype	Genotyp
germinal	germinal	germinal
ghetto	ghetto	Ghetto
good	bien	Gut
gravitational water	eaux d'infiltration	Sickerwasser
green belt	ceinture verte	Grüngürtel
gross national product	produit national brut	Bruttosozialprodukt
ground level concentration	concentration au niveau du sol	Konzentration am Boden
groundwater	eaux souterraines	Grundwasser
group behavior	comportement collectif	Gemeinshaftverhalten
gully erosion	ravinement	Ausfurchung
gustatory receptor	récepteur gustatif	Geschmackspore
habitat	habitat	Standort, Siedlungsraum
halogen	halogène	Halogen
health	santé	Gesundheit
hearing level	niveau de bruit	Lürapegel
hearing loss	perte d'audition	Hörverlust
hearing threshold level	niveau de bruit	Hörgrenze
herbicide	herbicide	Herbizid
heredity	hérédité	Vererbung
hertz	hertz	Hertz
heterotroph	organisme hétérotrophe	heterotrophischer Organismus

heterozygous	hétérozygote	heterozygot
homozygous	homozygote	homozygot
host	hôte	Wirt
house	maison	Haus
household	ménage	Haushalt
housing density	densité d'occupation des logements	Wohndichte
housing rehabilitation	rénovation du logement	Renovierung
human settlement	établissement humain	Siedlung
humification	humification	Humusbildung
humus	humus	Humus
hydrogeology	hydrogéologie	Hydrogeologie
hydrologic cycle	cycle naturel de l'eau	Wasserkreislauf
hydrology	hydrologie	Hydrologie
hydroponics	culture sans terre	Hydroponik
hydrosphere	hydrosphere	Hydrosphäre
hygiene	hygiène	Hygiene
immigration	immigration	Einwanderung
immunity	immunité	Immunität
impurity	impureté	Fremdstoff
incidence	incidence	Häufigkeit neuer Fälle
index of quality	indice de qualité	Qualität Index
indigenous	indigène	eingeboren
induced radioactivity	radioactivité induite	induzierte Radioaktivität
industrial waste water	eaux résiduaires industrielles	Industrieabwässer
industrial water	eau industrielle	Betriabswasser
infant mortality rate	taux de mortalité infantile	Kindersterblichkeitsquote
infection	infection	Infektion
infestation	infestation	Befall
infrasonic vibration	infrason	Infraschall
inherited trait	caractère héréditaire	Erbanlagen
insecticide	insecticide	Insektizid
integrated control	lutte intégrée	integrierte Schädlingsbekampfung
interspecific relation	relation interspecifique	interspezifische Beziehung
intertidal zone	zone intercotidale	zwischengezeitliche Zone
intraspecific relation	relation intraspecifique	intraspezifische Beziehung
ionizing radiation	rayonnement ionisant	ionisierende Teilchen

irradiation	irradiation	Bestrahlung
irrigation	irrigation	Bewässerung
irrigation water	eau d'irrigation	Bewässerungswasser
lake	lac	See
land clearing	défrichement	Rodung
land reclamation	restauration des terres	Urbarmachung
land subsidence	affaissement de terrain	Erdsenkung
land use density	densité d'occupation des sols	bebauter Prozentsatz
laterite	latérite	Laterit
laterization	latéritisation	Laterisierung
leaching	lessivage du sol	Laugung
lenitic	lentique	in stehenden Gewässern vorkommend
lentic	lentique	in stehenden Gewässern vorkommend
life expectancy	espérance de vie	Lebenserwartung
life style	train de vie	Lebensführung
limnetic	—	im Süsswasser vorkommend
limnology	limnologie	Limnologie
liquid waste	eaux usées	Abwässer
lithosphere	lithosphère	Lithosphäre
litter	litière du sol	Streu
littoral zone	zone littorale	—
local government	collectivité locale	Gebietskörperschaft
lotic	lotique	in fliessenden Gewässer vorkommend
lowest water level	étiage	niedrigster Wasserstand
lyophilization	lyophilisation	Gefrietertrocknung
macroclimate	macroclimat	Makroklima
macroeconomics	macroéconomie	Makroökonomik
malnutrition	malnutrition	Fehlernährung
marine sciences	sciences de la mer	Meereswissenschaft
market demand	demande marchande	Marktbedürfnis
market price	prix de marché	Marktpreis
marsh	marais	Moor
masked sound	son masqué	maskierter Schall
masking	effet de masque	Maskierungseffekt
masking sound	son masquant	maskierender Schall
master plan	schéma directeur d'aménagement et d'urbanisme	Flächennutzungsplan

mechanical vibration	vibration mécanique	mechanische Schwingung
megalopolis	conurbation	Ballungsgebeit
mental age	age mental	geistiges Alter
mental health	santé mentale	geistige Gesundheit
mesotrophic	mesotrophique	mesotrophisch
metabolic rate	taux de métabolisme	Grundumsatz
metabolism	métabolisme	Metabolismus
meteorology	météorologie	Meteorologie
metropolis	métropole	Hauptzentrum
metropolitan area	aire métropolitaine	Grossstadtgebiet
microclimate	microclimat	Mikroklima
microeconomics	microéconomie	Mikroökonomik
micronutrient	oligo-élément	Spurenelement
microorganism	micro-organisme	Mikroorganism
migration	migration	Wanderungsbewegung
mineral water	eau minérale	Mineralwasser
mixed layer	couche mixte	Mischschicht
mobile source	source mobile	bewegliche Quelle
model	modèle	Modell
molluscicide	molluscicide	Schneckengift
monitoring	surveillance continue	ständige Uberwachung
morbidity rate	taux de morbidité	Morbiditätsziffer
mortality rate	taux de mortalité	Sterbenziffer
mouth of a river	embouchure	Mündung
mulch	paillis	Dung
multifamily dwelling	habitation collective	Mehrfamilienhaus
mutagen	mutagène	Mutagen
mutant	mutant	Mutant
mutation	mutation	Mutation
mutation rate	taux de mutation	Mutationsziffer
mutualism	mutualisme	Mutualismus
mycotoxin	mycotoxine	Mykotoxin
national income	revenue national	Volkseinkommen
native	natif	Gebürtig
naturalization	naturalisation	Naturalisation
natural radiation	rayonnement naturel	natürliche Strahlung
natural radioactivity	radioactivité naturelle	natürliche Radio-aktivität
natural resource	ressource naturelle	Naturschätze
natural resource management	gestion des ressources naturelles	Naturschätzenutzung
natural selection	sélection naturelle	natürlische Auslese
nature preserve	réserve naturelle	Naturschutzgebiet
neighborhood	quartier	Viertel

neighborhood conservation	rénovation de quartier	Viertelssanierung
neighborhood unit	unité de voisinage	Nachbarschaftseinheit
nematocide	nématicide	Nematozid
net national product	produit national net	Nettosozialprodukt
net reproduction rate	taux de reproduction net	Nettoreproduktionhöhe
nitrification	nitrification	Nitrifikation
nitrogen cycle	cycle de l'azote	Stickstoffzyklus
nitrogen fixation	fixation de l'azote	Stickstoffbindung
noise	bruit	Geräusch
noise exposure forecast	indice isopsophique	isopsophischer Index
nonmonetary commodity	bien hors marché	Freigut
nonpoint source	source non-ponctuelle	Nichtpunktquelle
nonrenewable resource	ressource non-renouvelable	erschöpfliche Naturschätze
nuclear energy	énergie nucléaire	Kernenergie
nuclear fission	fission nucléaire	Kernspaltung
nuclear fuel	combustible nucléaire	Kernbrennstoff
nuclear fusion	fusion nucléaire	Kernfusion
nuclear pile	pile nucléaire	Kernreaktor
nuclear reaction	réaction nucléaire	Kernreaktion
nuclear reactor	réacteur nucléaire	Kernreaktor
nuclide	nucléide	Nuklid
number pyramid	pyramid des nombres	Zahlenpyramide
nutrient	nutriment	Nährstoff
nutrition	nutrition	Ernährung
oceanography	océanographie	Ozeanographie
oceanology	océanologie	Ozeanologie
oil dumping	décharge d'hydro-carbures	Ölablassen
oil pollution	pollution par les hydrocarbures	Ölverschmutzung
oil slick	tâche d'huile	Ölfleck
oil spill	déversement accidentel d'hydrocarbures	—
oligotrophic	oligotrophique	Oligotroph
open space	espace libre	Freiraum
organic farming	agriculture biologique	biologischdynamische Wirtschaftsweise
ovicide	ovicide	Ovizid
ozone layer	couche d'ozone	Ozonschicht

parasite	parasite	Parasit
parasitism	parasitisme	Parasitismus
particle detector	détecteur de rayonne-ment	Strahlungsanzeiger
particle velocity	vitesse acoustique	Schallgeschwindigkeit
particulate matter	particules solides	Staubteilchen
particulate	poussière	Staub
pathogen	agent pathogène	Pathogen
peak concentration	concentration de pointe	Spitzenkoncentration
pedogenesis	pédogénèse	Pedogenese
pedology	pédologie	Pedologie
pelagic	pélagique	pelagisch
penetrance	pénétrance	Eindringen
perceived noise level	niveau de son perçu	—
percolation	percolation	Sickerung
permanent resource	ressource permanente	unerschöpfliche Naturschätze
persistence	rémanence	Remanenz
pest	organisme nuisible	Ungeziefer
pest control	lutte contre les organismes nuisibles	Ungezieferbekämpfung
pesticide	pesticide	Pestizide
phenotype	phénotype	Phänotyp
photochemical smog	smog photochimique	photochemischer Smog
photosynthesis	photosynthèse	Photosynthese
physical control	lutte physique	physikalische Schädlingsbekämpfung
physical health	santé physique	Physischegesundheit
phytogeography	phytogéographie	Phytogeographie
phytoplankton	phytoplancton	Phytoplankton
phytotoxin	phytotoxine	Phytotoxin
plankter	—	—
plankton	plancton	Plankton
planning	planification	Planung
plant association	groupement végétal	Pflanzenfamilie
plant community	communauté végétal	Pflanzengesellshaft
pluralistic society	société pluraliste	pluralistische Gesellschaft
podzol	podzol	Podsol
podzolization	podzolisation	Podsolierung
point source	source ponctuelle	Punktquelle
pollutant	polluant	Schmutzstoff
pollution	pollution	Umweltverschmutzung
population	population, peuplement	Bevölkerung
population category	catégorie sociale	Gesellschaftsgruppe

population composition	composition d'une population	Bevölkerung Zusametzung
population density	densité de population	Bevölkerungsdichte
population dynamics	dynamique des populations	Bevölkerungdynamik
population genetics	génétique des populations	Populationsgenetik
population mobility	mobilité d'une population	Mobilität
population pyramid	pyramide des ages	Alterspyramid
precinct	quartier	Viertel
precipitation	précipitation	Niederschlag
predation	prédation	Episitie
predator	prédateur	Rauber
prevalence	prévalence	globale Häufigkeit
preventive medicine	médecine préventive	Präventivmedizin
prey	proie	Raub
price index	indice de prix	Index der Preise
primary production	production primaire	Primärproduktion
primary stage	stade primaire	erste Stufe
primitive area	réserve naturelle	Naturschutzgebiet
producer	producteur	Produzent
productivity	productivité	Produktivität
prophylaxis	prophylaxie	Vorbeugung
protein	protide	Protein
public health	santé publique	Gesundheitswesen
purchasing power	pouvoir d'achat	Kaufkraft
pure tone	son pur	reiner Ton
rad	rad	Rad
radiation	rayonnement	Strahlung
radiation detector	détecteur de rayonnement	Strahlungsanzeiger
radiation dosimetry	dosimétrie	Dosimetrie
radiation exposure	exposition	Strahlenbelastung
radiation injury	radiolésion	Strahlenschädigung
radiation monitoring	surveillance des rayonnements	Strahlenüberwachung
radiation source	source de rayonnement	Strahlungsquelle
radioactive contaminant	polluant radioactif	radioaktiver Schadstoff
radioactive contamination	contamination radioactive	radioaktiver Kontamination
radioactive decay	désintégration radioactive	radioaktiver Zerfall

radioactive decon- tamination	décontamination radioactive	radioaktive Dekontaminierung
radioactive element	élément radioactif	radioaktives Element
radioactive fallout	retombées	Fallout
radioactive half-life	période radioactive	radioaktive Halbwert- zeit
radioactive material	matière radioactive	aktives Material
radioactive series	activité nucléaire	Aktivität
radioactive source	source radioactive	radioaktive Strahlungs- quelle
radioactivity	radioactivité	Radioaktivität
radiobiology	radiobiologie	Radiobiologie
radioecology	radioécologie	Strahlenökologie
radiological con- tamination	contamination radiologique	radioaktive Kontamination
radiological decon- tamination	décontamination radiologique	radioaktive Dekontamination
radiological dose	dose radiologique	Strahlendosierung
radiology	radiologie	Radiologie
radionuclide	radionucleide	Radionuklid
rainfall	pluie	Regen
rainwater	eaux pluviales	Regenwasser
raw sewage	eaux usées nontraitées	Brackwasser
raw sludge	boues brutes	Frischschlamm
raw water	eau brute	Rohwasser
recessive	récessif	rezessiv
recycle	recycler	wiederverwenden
regimen	régime d'un cours d'eau	Abflussregime
regional plan	schéma directeur d'aménagement régional	Regionalplan
regional planning	aménagement regional	Regionalplanung
reliability	fiabilité	Zuverlässigkeit
rem	rem	Rem
renewable resource	ressource renouvelable	wiedererneuerbare Ressource
reproduction rate	taux de reproduction	Reproduktionshöhe
reservoir	réservoir	Reservoir
residual substance	résidu	Rückstand
residue	résidu	Rückstand
residuum	résidu	Rückstand
resistance	accoutumance	Anpassung
retention	rétention	Retention
reverberation	réverbération acoustique	Nachhall

rhizobium	rhizobium	Rhizobium
rill erosion	érosion en rigoles	—
rising stage	crue	Hochwasser
rodenticide	rodenticide	Rodentizid
roentgen	roentgen	Roentgen
row house	maison en bande	Reihenhaus
rural slum	taudis rural	—
saline soil	sol salin	Salzboden
salinity	salinité	Natriumchloridgehalt
salt content	teneur en sels	Salzgehalt
saltmarsh	marais salant	Meeressaline
sampling	prélèvement	Entnahme
sanitary engineering	génie sanitaire	Gesundheittechnik
sanitation	techniques sanitaires	Sanitärtechnik
saprophyte	saprophyte	Saprophyte
saprozoic	saprozoique, détritivore	—
satellite town	ville satellite	Satellitenstadt
savor	saveur	Geschmack
scrubber	épurateur	Skrubber
seasonal dwelling	résidence saisonière	Zweitwohnung
secondary production	production secondaire	Sekundärproduktion
second home	résidence secondaire	Zweitwohnung
sedimentation	sédimentation	Sedimentation
segregation	ségrégation	Segregation
semidetached house	habitation jumelée	Doppelhaus
separator	séparateur	Separator
service	service	Dienstleistungen
sewage sludge	boues d'épuration	Schlamm
shanty town	bidonville	Barackensiedlung
sheet erosion	érosion en nappe	—
sial	sial	Sial
silt	limon	Lehm
siltation	envasement	Verschlammung
sima	sima	Sima
simple tone	son pur	reiner Ton
single-family dwelling	habitation individuelle	Einfamilienhaus
site plan	plan de masse	Baumassenplan
slum	ilots insalubres	Elendsviertel
slum dwelling	taudis	Elendsquartier
slurb	—	—
smog	smog	Smog
smut	fumerons	Rauchholz
social behavior	comportement social	Verhalten

social benefit	avantage social	soziale Vorteil
social cost	coût social	soziale Kosten
social good	bien social	soziale Gut
social indicator	indicateur social	soziale Indikator
social integration	intégration	Integration
social mobility	mobilité sociale	soziale Verschiebung
society	société	Gesellschaft
soil	sol	Boden
soil conservation	restauration des sols	Bodenmelioration
soil depletion	épuisement du sol	Bodenerschöpfung
soil deterioration	dégradation du sol	Bodenzerstörung
soil fertility	fertilité	Fruchtbarkeit
soil genesis	pédogénèse	Bodenbildung
soil horizon	horizon pédologique	Bodenhorizont
soil improvement	amendement des sols	Melioration
soil mechanics	mécanique des sols	Bodentechnik
soil profile	profile	Profil
soil science	pédologie	Bodenforschung
somatic	somatique	somatisch
sonic boom	bang sonique	Überschallknall
soot	suies	Russ
sound	son	Schall
sound absorption	absorption acoustique	Schallabsorption
sound-absorption coefficient	facteur d'absorption acoustique	Schallabsorptionsfaktor
sound attenuation	atténuation acoustique	Schalldämpfung
sound energy	énergie acoustique	Schallenergie
sound-energy flux density	intensité acoustique	Schallintensität
sound intensity	intensité acoustique	Schallintensität
sound-intensity level	niveau d'intensité acoustique	Schallintensitätspegel
sound level	niveau acoustique pondéré	Schallpegel
sound-level meter	sonomètre	Lautstärkemesser
sound power	puissance acoustique	Schalleistung
sound-power desnity	intensité acoustique	Schallintensität
sound-power level	niveau de puissance acoustique	Schalleistungspegel
sound pressure	pression acoustique	Schalldruck
sound-pressure level	niveau de pression acoustique	Schalldruckpegel
sound spectrum	spectre d'un bruit	Schallspektrum
source of emission	source d'émission	Schadstoff Quelle
source of pollution	source de pollution	Verschmutzungsquelle

specific absorbed dose	dose absorbée specifique	spezifische absorbierte Dosis
spectrogram	spectrogramme	Spektrogramm
spillover	retombée	—
spoil bank	terril	Halde
spoil heap	terril	Halde
spring	source	Quelle
squatter settlement	installation de squatters	—
stack solids	envols	Auswurf
standard	norme	Norm
standard of consumption	niveau de consommation	Verbrauchseinkeit
standard of living	niveau de vie	Lebensstandard
static pressure	pression statique	statischer Druck
stationary source	source stationaire	stationär Quelle
stratum	horizon pédologique	Bodenhorizont
streamflow	débit d'un cours d'eau	Durchfluss
street furniture	mobilier urbain	—
subsonic	subsonique	unterschall
subsurface drainage	drainage souterrain	—
subsurface water	eaux souterraines	Grundwasser
suburb	banlieue	Aussenbezirk
supersonic	supersonique	überschall
surface-active agent	agent de surface	grenzflächenaktiver Waschmittelzusatz
surface drainage	drainage de surface	—
surface mining	travail de mine à ciel ouvert	Tagebau
surface runoff	eaux de ruissellement	Rieselwasser
surface water	eaux de surface	Oberflächenwasser
surfactant	agent de surface	grenzflächenaktiver Waschmittelzusatz
suspended solid	particule en suspension	suspendierte Stoffe
suspension	suspension	Aufschlämmung
swamp	marécage	Moor
symbiosis	symbiose	Symbiose
synecology	synécologie	Biozökologie
synergism	synergie	Synergie
tailings	résidus de mine	Rückstaude
teratogen	agent tératogène	Teratogen
territoriality	territorialité	Territorialität
territory	territoire	Gabiet

thermal effluent	effluent thermique	—
thermal environment	environnement thermique	—
thermal pollution	pollution thermique	—
thermonuclear fusion	fusion thermonucléaire	Kernverschmelzung
thermopollution	pollution thermique	—
threshold	seuil	Schwellenwert
threshold of audibility	seuil d'audition	Hörschwelle
threshold of detectability	seuil d'audition	Hörschwelle
threshold of discomfort	niveau acoustique de gène	Schallpegel an der Verträglichkeitsgrenze
threshold of feeling	niveau acoustique de sensation	Gefühlgrenze
threshold of pain	niveau acoustique de douleur	Schmerzgrenze
tidal wetlands	marais maritime	Seemarsh
tideland	estran	Gezeitenzone
tolerance	tolérance	Toleranz
tolerance limit	seuil de tolérance	Toleranzgrenze
toxicology	toxicologie	Toxikologie
toxin	toxine	Toxine
town	ville	Stadt
town house	maison en bande	städtische Haus
trace element	elément-trace	Spurenelemente
trauma	trauma	Trauma
treated sewage	eaux usées traitées	—
trophic accumulation	accumulation trophique	tropisch Akkumulation
trophic level	niveau trophique	trophisches Niveau
turbidity	turbidité	Trübung
two-family dwelling	duplex	Doppelhaus
ultrasonic vibration	ultrason	Ultraschall
urban community	communauté urbaine	Gemeinschaft
urban design	esthétique urbaine	städtebauliche Gestaltung
urban infrastructure	infrastructure urbaine	städtische Infrastruktur
urbanization	urbanisation	Verstädterung
urbanized area	agglomération urbaine	städtische Siedlung
urbanizing area	aire en cours d'urbanisation	Verstädterungsgebiet
urban plan	schéma directeur d'aménagement et d'urbanisme	Flächennutzungsplan

urban planning	urbanisme, planifi- cation urbaine	Städteplanung
urban redevelopment	rénovation urbaine	Städtsanierung
urban renewal	réhabilitation urbaine	Wiederestellung
urban sociology	sociologie urbaine	städtische Soziologie
vector	vecteur	Vektor
village	village	Dorf
virucide	virulicide	Virusgift
want	besoin	Bedarf
washer	laveur	Waschapparat
waste	déchet	Abfälle
waste water	eaux usées	Abwässer
water catchment	adduction d'eau	Wasserversorgungsan- lage
water divide	ligne de partage des eaux	Wasserscheide
water erosion	érosion hydraulique	Wassererosion
water hardness	dureté d'une eau	Härte
water holding capacity	capacité de retention en eau	Rückhaltevermögen
water purification	—	—
water quality	qualité de l'eau	Wasserqualität
water resource management	gestion des eaux	Wasserwirtschaft
watershed	bassin fluvial	Einzugsgebiet
water softening	adoucissement	Enthärtung
water supply	provision d'eau	Wasservorkommen
water table	surface phréatique	Grundwasserspiegel
water treatment	traitement de l'eau	Wasseraufbereitung
well-being	bien être	Wohlbefinden
wet collector	laveur	—
wetlands	terrains marécageux	—
wilderness area	réserve naturelle	Naturschutzgebiet
wildlife refuge	refuge zoologique	—
wild river	rivière protégée	—
wind erosion	érosion éolienne	Winderosion
yield	rendement des sols	Ertrag
zone	zone	Gebiet
zone of aeration	zone d'aération	Beluftungzone
zone of saturation	zone de saturation	Sättigungszone
zoning	zonage	Zoneneinteilung

zoning map	plan d'occupation des sols	Masseplanzone
zoogeography	zoogéographie	Zoogeographie
zooplankton	zooplancton	Zooplankton
zootoxin	zootoxine	Zootoxin

AIR AND CLIMATE

acid smog, 64*
aerosol, 3, 33, 64, 67
aerosol propellant, 3
atmosphere, 6, 3, 8, 10, 11, 35,
 38, 39, 41, 46, 54, 57, 59, 64, 70
atmospheric sciences, 41

climate, 12, 1, 12, 38
climatic region, 12
climatic zone, 12

dispersion model, 19, 43
droplet, 20
dust separator, 20

fly ash, 29

ground-level concentration, 33

halogen, 33, 61

macroclimate, 12
meteorology, 41
microclimate, 12

ozone layer, 3

particulate, 49, 29, 70
particulate matter, 49, 20, 72
photochemical smog, 64

scrubber, 62
smog, 64
smut, 64
soot, 67, 64
stack solids, 70

washer, 62
wet collector, 62

ECOLOGY AND BIOLOGY

abiotic, 10
acclimatation, 1
acclimatization, 1
accumulation, 1, 26, 74
adaptation, 2, 1, 65
aerobic, 3, 46, 63
age, 3, 18, 53
aging process, 3
algicide, 51

allogenic, 4
ammonification, 46
anaerobic, 3, 28, 63
animal association, 8
animal community, 8, 45
antitoxin, 74
autecology, 21
autochthonous, 36
autotroph, 7, 9

---

*The definition of a term will be found at the initial page number
listed, either as a main entry or underscored within the definition of
a main entry.

bacterial toxin, 74
bactericide, 51
biocenose, 7, 9, 10, 21, 22, 73
biocide, 51
biodegradable, 8, 18, 50
biodynamic, 21
biogeochemical cycle, 8, 11, 17
 44, 46
biogeography, 8
biological age, 3
biological balance, 9
biological control, 50
biological cycle, 9
biological half-life, 9
biological indicator, 9
biological production, 9, 44
biological productivity, 9
biology, 9, 58
biomass, 9, 21, 41
biomass pyramid, 21
biome, 10, 53
biosphere, 10, 8
biota, 10, 73, 79
biotic, 10, 8, 24
biotic community, 8
biotope, 10, 8, 9, 22, 36, 73

carbon cycle, 11, 8
carrying capacity, 11
chemical control, 50
chemical weathering, 17, 62, 66
chemosynthesis, 12, 7
chronological age, 3
climax, 10
commensalism, 13, 21
concentration, 1, 9, 28, 38, 56
consumer, 29, 21
corrosion, 17
cultural practices, 50-51
cumulative effect, 1, 51

decomposer, 17
decomposition, 17, 63, 65
defoliant, 17
degree of adaptability, 2

denaturation, 55
denitrification, 46
desiccant, 17
dominance, 19, 8, 10
drying agent, 17

ecological community, 8
ecological interaction, 21, 9, 13,
 19, 49, 54
ecological niche, 21
ecological pyramid, 21
ecology, 21, 58
ecosystem, 22, 4, 9, 10, 11, 19,
 26, 29, 38, 75, 80
ecotone, 22
ectoparasite, 49
edaphon, 23
endangered species, 24
endogenous, 24
endoparasite, 49
endotoxin, 74
energy pyramid, 21
enzyme, 25, 28
ethology, 26
exogenous, 24
exotoxin, 74

fermentation, 28
ferment, 28
food chain, 29, 1, 9, 21, 52, 56
food web, 29
forest management, 30
forestry, 30
fungicide, 51
fungus, 30, 42, 74

habitat, 33, 7, 9, 21, 24, 26, 30, 79
herbicide, 51
heterotroph, 34, 9, 17, 30
host, 49, 50, 77

indigenous, 36
infestation, 50, 49
insecticide, 51
integrated control, 51

interspecific relation, 21
intraspecific relation, 21

mental age, 3
metabolic rate, 41
metabolism, 41, 25
microorganism, 42, 8, 12, 17, 28, 36, 46, 49
molluscicide, 51
mycotoxin, 74

native, 36
naturalization, 1
natural resource, 44, 11, 21, 22, 24
natural resource management, 44
nature preserve, 45
nematocide, 51
nitrification, 46
nitrogen cycle, 46, 8
nitrogen fixation, 46
nonrenewable resource, 44
number pyramid, 21

ovicide, 51

parasite, 49, 30, 50
parasitism, 49, 21
peak concentration, 1
permanent resource, 44
persistence, 50, 51
pest, 50
pest control, 50, 51
pesticide, 51, 49, 50, 60
photosynthesis, 51, 7, 11, 55
physical control, 50
phytogeography, 8
phytotoxin, 74
plant association, 8
plant community, 8, 45

population, 53, 11, 21, 24, 80
predation, 54, 21, 24
predator, 54, 50
prey, 54
primary production, 9
primary stage, 9
primitive area, 80
producer, 29, 21
protein, 55, 25, 31, 47, 52

renewable resource, 44
residual substance, 60, 28
resistance, 60
retention, 1
rhizobium, 46
rodenticide, 51

saprophyte, 34, 30
saprozoic, 34
secondary production, 9
symbiosis, 21
synecology, 21

territoriality, 72
territory, 72
tolerance, 74
tolerance limit, 74, 1
toxicology, 74
toxin, 74
trauma, 74
trophic accumulation, 1
trophic level, 29, 1, 9, 21, 50

virucide, 51

wild river, 80
wilderness area, 80
wildlife refuge, 80

zoogeography, 8
zootoxin, 74

ECONOMICS

capital good, 32
commodity, 32
consumer, 14
consumer good, 32
consumer society, 14
consumption, 14, 21, 22, 77, 79
cost of living, 70
cost-benefit analysis, 15
cost-effectiveness analysis, 15

demand schedule, 40

econometrics, 21
economic development, 21
economic expansion, 22
economic good, 32, 40, 63
economic growth, 22
economics, 22, 21, 32, 63, 77
economic unit, 22, 27, 32, 44, 65
effective demand, 40
effectiveness, 23, 15
efficiency, 23, 15, 55
external diseconomy, 27
external economy, 27
externality, 27

factor of production, 23, 55
free good, 32

good, 32, 14, 22, 23, 32, 44, 55,
56, 70, 77
gross national product, 32, 22

life style, 70, 33

macroeconomics, 22
market demand, 40
market price, 40, 32, 56
microeconomics, 22

national income, 44
net national product, 32
nonmonetary commodity, 32

price index, 56
productivity, 55, 45, 80
purchasing power, 56, 70

service, 63, 22, 32, 44, 63, 64, 70, 76
social benefit, 65, 26, 27
social cost, 65, 26, 27, 32
social good, 32
spillover, 27
standard of consumption, 70
standard of living, 70

want, 77, 14, 40

FOOD

assimilation, 6, 40, 47

dietary deficiency, 18
dietetics, 18

feedstuff, 30
flavor, 28, 29
food, 29, 4, 18, 19, 29, 40, 41,
47, 49, 51, 60, 72
food additive, 29
food irradiation, 29

food product, 30
foodstuff, 30, 29
freeze drying, 40

gustatory receptor, 62

lyophilization, 40

malnutrition, 40
micronutrient, 42

108

nutrient, 47, 4, 6, 7, 26, 28,
  29, 66
nutriment, 29
nutrition, 47, 18, 40

savor, 62

trace element 42

GENETICS

chromosome, 12, 30

DNA molecule, 12, 43
dominance, 19

ecotype, 22
expressivity, 26

gene, 30, 19, 26, 31, 44, 59
gene pool, 31, 53
genetic damage, 31
genetic inheritance, 31, 34
genetic load, 31
genetic map, 30
genetic polymorphism, 31, 45, 54
genetics, 31
genetic variation, 31, 45
genotype, 31, 26, 44, 45, 50, 51
germinal, 67

heredity, 34, 14
heterozygous, 19
homozygous, 19, 59

inherited trait, 37, 19, 26, 31, 50,
  59, 64

mutagen, 43
mutant, 44
mutation, 44, 31, 43, 45
mutation rate, 44

natural selection, 45, 31

penetrance, 50
phenotype, 51, 44
population genetics, 54

recessive, 59

somatic, 67

HEALTH

adjuvant treatment, 3
age-specific death rate, 43, 39
allergen, 4, 33
allergy, 4, 46
anaphylaxis, 4
anomaly, 5, 72

carcinogen, 11
case fatality rate, 43
congenital, 14, 5, 72
contagion, 15
crude death rate, 43

death rate, 43
death rate by cause of death, 43
disinfectant, 19

endemism, 24
environmental health, 24, 61, 62
epidemic, 25
epidemiology, 25

health, 33, 18, 24, 29, 35, 55, 56, 79
hygiene, 35

immunity, 4
incidence, 43, 25
infant mortality rate, 43
infection, 36

mental health, 33
morbidity rate, 43
mortality rate, 43

pathogen, 49, 19, 33, 36, 77
physical health, 33

prevalence, 43, 24
preventive medicine, 55
prophylaxis, 55
public health, 56

sanitation, 62
somatic, 67

teratogen, 72

vector, 77

HUMAN SETTLEMENTS

apartment house, 34

buffer strip, 48
buffer zone, 48

city, 12, 14, 41, 45, 48, 64, 71, 76
community design, 75
community facility, 13, 45, 75, 76, 77
community plan, 76
comprehensive plan, 76
conurbation, 41

detached house, 34
development plan, 76
dormitory suburb, 71
duplex, 34
dwelling, 20, 53, 62, 64
dwelling unit, 20, 53

exurb, 71

futurology, 30

general plan, 76
ghetto, 64
green belt, 48

habitat, 33
house, 34

household, 20, 22
housing rehabilitation, 34, 77
human settlement, 35, 12, 75

local government, 40, 12, 75, 76, 81

master plan, 76
megalopolis, 41
metropolis, 42, 35, 41, 63
metropolitan area, 42
multifamily dwelling, 20

neighborhood, 45, 14, 52, 77
neighborhood conservation, 77
neighborhood unit, 45

open space, 48

planning, 52
precinct, 45

regional plan, 76
regional planning, 76, 52
row house, 34
rural slum, 64

satellite town, 71
seasonal dwelling, 62
second home, 62
semidetached house, 34

shanty town, 63
single-family dwelling, 20
site plan, 76
slum, 64, 76
slum dwelling, 64
slurb, 64
squatter settlement, 63
street furniture, 75
suburb, 71, 64, 76

town, 12, 40
town house, 34
two-family dwelling, 20

urban community, 75, 13, 77

urban design, 75
urban infrastructure, 76, 77
urbanization, 76, 41
urbanized area, 76, 42
urbanizing area, 76
urban plan, 76, 81
urban planning, 76, 45, 52
urban redevelopment, 76, 77
urban renewal, 77

village, 12, 35, 40

zone, 80
zoning, 81
zoning map, 81

LAND AND SOIL

aggregate, 4

compost, 14
crop rotation, 16

edaphic, 23

fallow land, 27
fertilizer, 28, 26, 49, 71

humification, 35
humus, 35

land clearing, 38
land reclamation, 38, 69, 71, 79
land subsidence, 38
laterite, 38
laterization, 38
lithosphere, 39, 8, 10, 35
litter, 39, 52

mulch, 39

organic farming, 49
pedogenesis, 66
pedology, 67
podzol, 52

podzolization, 52, 66

saline soil, 61
sedimentation, 62, 63
sial, 39
silt, 63
siltation, 63
sima, 39
soil, 65, 2, 4, 5, 6, 13, 14, 17, 23, 25, 27,
   28, 35, 38, 45, 46, 51, 66, 67, 78, 80
soil conservation, 66
soil depletion, 66, 16
soil deterioration, 66, 80
soil fertility, 66
soil genesis, 66
soil horizon, 66
soil improvement, 66
soil mechanics, 66
soil profile, 66
soil science, 67
spoil bank, 69
spoil heap, 69, 38
stratum, 66, 62
surface mining, 71

tailings, 72, 71
yield, 80, 20, 28, 37

MULTIDISCIPLINARY TERMS

activated carbon, 2
activated charcoal, 2
adjuvant, 2
adulterant, 36
aeration, 3, 6, 63
aerator, 3
ambiance, 5

by-product, 77, 60

comfort, 13, 70
comfort zone, 13
contaminant, 15
contamination, 15
criterion, 16
critical, 73

discomfort, 13, 2, 27, 73

emission, 23, 18, 19, 53, 56,
58, 64
environment, 24, 5, 10, 11, 15,
16, 19, 21, 22, 24, 25, 30, 33,
37, 42, 44, 50, 53, 57, 58, 59,
64, 65, 67, 68, 69, 76, 77, 79
environmental indicator, 24
exposure, 26, 1, 3, 24, 36, 37,
38, 56

fatigue, 27, 3

impurity, 36
index of quality, 25

mobile source, 23
model, 42
monitoring, 43, 25, 79
mutualism, 72, 44, 21

nonpoint source, 23

point source, 23
pollutant, 53, 1, 9, 15, 17, 19, 23, 26,
33, 39, 50, 64, 71
pollution, 53, 8, 23, 25, 33, 38, 48,
63, 69, 71, 77

recycle, 77,
reliability, 59
residue, 60
residuum, 60

sampling, 61
separator, 63
source of emission, 23
source of pollution, 23
standard, 16, 5
stationary source, 23
synergism, 72

threshold, 73, 25

waste, 77, 8, 11, 15, 39, 60, 61,
69, 71, 72
well-being, 79, 11, 13, 53, 70

NOISE AND VIBRATIONS

acoustic disturbance, 2
acoustic power, 68
acoustics, 2
acoustic signal, 2
acoustic vibration, 2, 6, 64, 67
ambient noise, 5, 2, 7

audio frequency, 6, 36, 68, 75
audiogram, 6, 7
audiometer, 6
audio range, 6
auditory environment, 7, 5
auditory sensation area, 7

background noise, 7

community noise equivalent
 level, 46
community noise rating, 46
complex tone, 14

decibel, 17, 41, 68, 69, 73

environmental noise, 7
equivalent sound level, 68

hearing level, 33, 6
hearing loss, 33
hearing threshold level, 33
hertz, 6

infrasonic vibration, 36

masked sound, 41
masking, 41
masking sound, 41
mechanical vibration, 41

noise, 46, 2, 67, 69
noise exposure forecast, 46

particle velocity, 49
perceived noise level, 50, 46
pure tone, 64

reverberation, 60

simple tone, 64
sonic boom, 67
sound, 67, 2, 5, 7, 14, 36, 46, 49,
 60, 64, 67, 69, 75
sound absorption, 67, 60
sound-absorption coefficient, 67
sound attenuation, 67
sound energy, 67, 68
sound-energy flux density, 68
sound intensity, 68, 67
sound-intensity level, 68
sound level, 68, 50, 67, 69
sound-level meter, 68
sound power, 68
sound-power density, 68
sound-power level, 68, 17
sound pressure, 68
sound-pressure level, 69, 68, 73
sound spectrum, 69, 14
spectrogram, 69
static pressure, 70, 68
subsonic, 36
supersonic, 75

threshold of audibility, 73, 7, 33, 41
threshold of detectability, 73
threshold of discomfort, 73
threshold of feeling, 73
threshold of pain, 73, 7

ultrasonic vibration, 75

RADIOACTIVITY

absorbed dose, 1, 19, 56
artificial radioactivity, 6
atomic pile, 47
atomic reactor, 47

background radiation, 7

cosmic radiation, 15, 7
cosmic rays, 15
curie, 58

decontamination factor, 57
dose equivalent, 19, 56
dose equivalent rate, 20
dosimeter, 20, 57

effective half-life, 23
exposure dose, 56

fast breeder reactor, 27
fertile material, 28, 27, 47

fissile material, 28
fissionable material, 28, 27, 47

induced radioactivity, 36
ionizing radiation, 37, 1, 7, 15, 19, 20, 29, 36, 37, 44, 49, 56, 57, 58
irradiation, 37

natural radiation, 44, 7
natural radioactivity, 44
nuclear energy, 46
nuclear fission, 47, 28
nuclear fuel, 47, 27
nuclear fusion, 47
nuclear pile, 47
nuclear reaction, 47, 6, 37, 46
nuclear reactor, 47, 27
nuclide, 47, 23, 57, 58

particle detector, 49, 57

rad, 1, 19
radiation, 56, 6, 23, 37, 50, 55
radiation detector, 49
radiation dosimetry, 56
radiation exposure, 56, 15, 26
radiation injury, 56
radiation monitoring, 57

radiation source, 57
radioactive contaminant, 58, 57
radioactive contamination, 57, 58
radioactive decay, 57, 23, 36, 47, 58
radioactive decontamination, 57
radioactive element, 57, 43
radioactive fallout, 57
radioactive half-life, 57
radioactive material, 57, 50, 58
radioactive series, 58
radioactive source, 58
radioactivity, 58, 6, 36, 44, 47, 50, 56, 57
radiobiology, 58
radioecology, 58
radiological contamination, 57
radiological decontamination, 57
radiological dose, 1
radiology, 58
radionuclide, 47, 44, 58
rem, 20
roentgen, 56, 20

specific absorbed dose, 1

thermonuclear fusion, 47

SOCIETY AND POPULATION

age interval, 53
age-specific birth rate, 10
anomie, 5

birth rate, 10

community participation, 13
crude birth rate, 10

demography, 17
desegregation, 65

emigration, 42

family planning, 27, 10
fecundity, 10
fertility, 10, 38, 61, 66

group behavior, 65

housing density, 53

immigration, 42

land use density, 53
life expectancy, 39

migration, 42, 45, 63

net reproduction rate, 10

pluralistic society, 52
population, 53, 2, 10, 17, 24,
  25, 31, 35, 39, 43, 45, 53, 54,
  60, 63, 64, 65, 76, 77
population category, 53, 39
population composition, 53, 10
population density, 53

population dynamics, 54
population mobility, 54
population pyramid, 53

reproduction rate, 10

segregation, 65
social behavior, 64, 5
social indicator, 25
social integration, 65
social mobility, 65
society, 65, 5, 22, 30, 32, 44, 52

urban sociology, 77

WATER

activated sludge, 63
alga, 4, 9, 42
algae bloom, 4
alluvial deposit, 4
alluvion, 4
alluvium, 4
aquaculture, 5
aquiculture, 5
aquifer, 6, 33

benthic, 7
benthos, 7
biochemical oxygen demand, 8
black tide, 48
BOD test, 8, 11

catchment area, 20
chemical oxygen demand, 11
chlorinity, 61
coastal zone, 12, 80
COD test, 11
colloid, 13
colluvium, 13

dam, 16, 78, 80
detergent, 18, 71
diffusion, 72

digested sludge, 63
discharge, 18, 23, 48, 73, 80
dispersion, 72
dispersion medium, 13
domestic waste, 39
domestic water, 79, 78
drainage, 20, 38, 61
drainage basin, 20, 71
drinking water, 79

effluent, 39, 26, 63, 80
emulsion, 72
erosion, 25, 4, 30, 63, 66
estuary, 25
eutrophic, 26
eutrophication, 26, 28, 38, 52

falling stage, 18
field capacity, 78
flocculant, 75, 13
flocculation, 75, 63
floccule, 75
flocs, 75
flood stage, 18

gravitational water, 78
ground water, 33, 35, 38, 69

gully erosion, 25

hydrogeology, 35
hydrologic cycle, 35, 54
hydrology, 35
hydroponics, 6
hydrosphere, 35, 8, 10, 39

industrial waste water, 39
industrial water, 79, 78
intertidal zone, 74
irrigation, 37, 16, 61, 78
irrigation water, 79

lake, 37, 20, 26, 39, 48, 63, 71
leaching, 38, 28, 52, 66, 69
lenitic, 39
lentic, 39
limnetic, 50
limnology, 39
liquid waste, 39, 8, 11, 14, 63, 78
littoral zone, 12
lotic, 39
lowest water level, 18

marine sciences, 48
marsh, 79
mesotrophic, 26
mineral water, 33
mixed layer, 71

oceanography, 48, 71
oceanology, 48
oil dumping, 48
oil pollution, 48
oil slick, 48
oil spill, 48
oligotrophic, 26

pelagic, 50
percolation, 38
phytoplankton, 52, 26
plankter, 52
plankton, 52

precipitation, 54, 72, 13, 20, 25, 35, 57, 59, 71

rainfall, 59, 37, 38, 54, 78
rainwater, 59
raw sewage, 39, 63
raw sludge, 63
raw water, 79
regimen, 59, 16
reservoir, 38, 16, 63, 73
rill erosion, 25
rising stage, 18
river mouth, 25

salinity, 61, 78
salt content, 61
saltmarsh, 80
sanitary engineering, 61
sewage sludge, 63
sheet erosion, 25
spring, 69, 6
streamflow, 18
subsurface drainage, 20
subsurface water, 33, 73
surface-active agent, 71
surface drainage, 20
surface runoff, 71, 13, 20, 25, 37
surface water, 71, 35
surfactant, 71, 18
suspended solid, 75, 72
suspension, 72, 3, 13, 18, 20, 49, 63, 75
swamp, 80

thermal effluent, 73
thermal environment, 73
thermal pollution, 73
thermopollution, 73
tidal wetlands, 74, 80
tideland, 74, 48
treated sewage, 39
turbidity, 75, 26, 78

waste water, 39

water catchment, 78
water cycle, 35
water diversion, 78, 80
water divide, 20
water erosion, 25
water hardness, 78
water-holding capacity, 78
water purification, 79
water quality, 78
water resource management, 79
watershed, 20, 30

water softening, 78, 79
water supply, 79, 78
water table, 33
water treatment, 79, 78
wetlands, 79, 20, 74
wind erosion, 25

zone of aeration, 6
zone of saturation, 6
zooplankton, 52

ABOUT THE AUTHORS

PAUL BRACE was a member of the panel that wrote the Vocabulaire de l'Environnement, published in France, which he has translated and adapted for U.S. usage. At that time he was Urban Affairs Officer at the U.S. Embassy in Paris and coordinator of the U.S.-French program on new towns and the urban environment. He is now program manager in environmental research for the U.S. Department of Housing and Urban Development in Washington, D.C. Previously he has been a planner on the city, county, and state levels, and has worked abroad in Morocco, Chile, and France. He has been a visiting professor of planning in New York, California, Washington, D.C., and France, and has co-authored environmental and planning publications. He holds a French Baccalaureat es Lettres, a B.S. in Landscape Architecture and an M.S. in City and Regional Planning from the University of Michigan. He has served on planning and environmental committees of several international organizations, and is a member of various professional societies in these fields.

RENÉ DUBOS, who wrote the Foreword, is internationally recognized for his outstanding work in bacteriology and the human environment. His work and his writings on these subjects have brought him numerous honorary degrees and awards, including the Robert Koch Centennial award and the Pulitzer prize, 1969. Professor Dubos was born in France where he completed his undergraduate studies. He received a Ph.D. from Rutgers University and in 1927 joined the Rockefeller Institute (now Rockefeller University), of which he is now Professor Emeritus.

The CONSEIL INTERNATIONALE DE LA LANGUE FRANÇAISE, a Paris-based organization, has produced a number of scientific and technical glossaries in an effort to keep the French language abreast of developments in these fields. In 1970, the Council commissioned a group of distinguished experts in the diverse environmental disciplines to author a glossary of environmental terms. Their Vocabulaire de l'Environnement was published for the U.N. Conference on the Environment in Stockholm, in 1972, and a revised edition was published in 1976. It forms the basis for this glossary, which has been expanded and adapted for U.S. use, and for a German edition soon to be published in West Germany.

The members of the panel of the <u>Vocabulaire de l'Environnement</u> were:

J. Ternisien, Chairman	Science Advisor, Ministry of the Quality of Life; Science Advisor, National Agency for Scientific and Technical Research, Paris
R. Amavis, Vice Chairman	Principal Administrator, European Communities Commission, Luxembourg
S. Dumesnil, Secretary	International Council of the French Language, Paris
P. Brace	Urban Affairs Officer, U.S. Embassy, Paris
A. de Chauveron	Director, French Standardization Association, Paris
P. Chovin	Director, National Police Laboratories, Paris
R. Colas	Technical Advisor, Institute for Sanitary Techniques, National School of Arts and Trades, Paris
J. Crepey	Director of Research, Scientific and Technical Institute of Marine Fisheries, Nantes
A. Denner	Psychologist, Communication Techniques, National Education Ministry; Professor, Special School of Architecture, Paris
R. Devouge	Consulting Engineer, Association for the Development of Environmental Sciences and Techniques, Paris
A. Esban	Information Division, World Health Organization, Geneva
J. G. Faugère	Director, Municipal Laboratories, Bordeaux
G. Giles	President, Association for the Development of Environmental Sciences and Techniques, Paris
Dr. L. Grange	Pollution Prevention Service, Ministry of the Quality of Life, Paris
Dr. S. W. A. Gunn	Chief, Service of Terminology, World Health Organization, Geneva
P. Jacquard	Chief of Research, National Center for Scientific Research, Center for the Study of Ecology and Plant Communities, Montpellier

Dr. Lacambre	National Council for Public Hygiene, Paris
P. Laurent	Deputy Director of Research, National Center for Scientific Research; Director of Limnological Hydrobiology, Thonon
J. Mattei	Civil Engineer; Chief, Department of Acoustics and Vibrations, National Electricity Administration, Paris
J. B. Perrin	Director, Agency for Trees and Green Space, Ministry of Equipment (Urban Development), Paris
M. Philippart-Denisot	Deputy Chief Editor, Agricultural Sciences, Documentation Center, National Center for Scientific Research, Paris
R. Piboubes	Chief, Documentation Service, National Bureau for Oceanic Data, National Center for the Exploitation of the Oceans, Paris
A. Roussel	Professor of Preventive and Social Medicine; Chairman, Scientific Committee for Atmospheric Pollution, Interministerial Commission for Nature and Environment, Paris
Dr. A. Sliosberg	Lexicographer and Translator, Paris
D. Yon	Museum of Natural History, Paris

CLEANING UP EUROPE'S WATERS: Economics,
Management, and Policies
>
> Ralph W. Johnson
> Gardner M. Brown, Jr.

THE ENERGY CRISIS AND THE ENVIRONMENT:
An International Perspective
>
> edited by
> Donald R. Kelley

*THE ENERGY CRISIS AND U.S. FOREIGN POLICY
>
> edited by
> Joseph S. Szyliowicz
> Bard E. O'Neill

ENVIRONMENTAL LEGISLATION: A Sourcebook
>
> edited by
> Mary Robinson Sive

*Also available in paperback as a PSS Student Edition